Science

for the GED® Test

New Readers Press®
ProLiteracy's publishing division

Science for the GED® Test
ISBN: 978-1-56420-755-5

Copyright© 2015 New Readers Press
New Readers Press
ProLiteracy's Publishing Division
104 Marcellus Street, Syracuse, New York 13204
www.newreaderspress.com

Printed in the United States of America
10   9   8   7   6   5   4   3

Proceeds from the sale of New Readers Press materials support professional
development, training, and technical assistance programs of ProLiteracy that
benefit local literacy programs in the U.S. and around the globe.

Editorial Director: Terrie Lipke
Technology Specialist: Maryellen Casey

GED® is a registered trademark of the American Council on Education (ACE)
and administered exclusively by GED Testing Service LLC under license. This
material is not endorsed or approved by ACE or GED Testing Service.

Contents

About the GED® Science Test 4

Unit 1: Life Science

Lesson 1: Organization of Life 5
    Cell Theory 5
    Essential Functions of Life 6
    Energy for Life Functions 7
    Mitosis and Meiosis 8
    Guided Practice 10

Lesson 2: Genetics and Heredity 11
    Central Dogma of Molecular Biology 11
    Genotypes and Phenotypes 12
    New Alleles, Assortment of Alleles 13
    Guided Practice 15

Lesson 3: Human Body and Health 16
    Body Systems 16
    Homeostasis 18
    Sources of Nutrients 19
    Transmission of Disease 20
    Guided Practice 21

Lesson 4: Evolution 22
    Common Ancestry 22
    Selection 25
    Adaptation 27
    Guided Practice 28

Lesson 5: Ecosystems 29
    Flow of Energy in Ecosystems 29
    Flow of Matter in Ecosystems 30
    Carrying Capacity 31
    Symbiosis 32
    Disruption of Ecosystems 33
    Guided Practice 34

Unit 1 Practice 36

Unit 2: Physical Science

Lesson 1: Motion and Forces 41
    Speed 41
    What Is a Force? 43
    Work and Machines 45
    Guided Practice 47

Lesson 2: Matter 48
    The Structure of Matter 48
    Physical and Chemical Properties 49
    Balancing Chemical Equations 51
    Solutions 53
    Guided Practice 54

Lesson 3: Energy 55
    Heat 55
    Exothermic and Endothermic Reactions 57
    Types of Energy 58
    Sources of Energy 60
    Waves 62
    Guided Practice 64

Unit 2 Practice 67

Unit 3: Earth and Space Science

Lesson 1: Earth and Its Systems 73
    Characteristics of the Atmosphere 73
    Characteristics of the Ocean 74
    Interaction Between Earth's Systems 75
    The Structure of Earth 76
    The Age of Earth 78
    Guided Practice 79

Lesson 2: Interactions Between Earth and Living Things 81
    Interactions Between Living and Nonliving Things 81
    Extraction and Use of Natural Resources 83
    Natural Hazards 84
    Guided Practice 85

Lesson 3: The Cosmos 86
    Structures in the Universe 86
    Sun, Planets, and Moons 88
    Guided Practice 90

Unit 3 Practice 91

Practice Test 96

Answer Key 108

About the GED® Science Test

The GED test is designed to measure your understanding of content areas that are recognized as most useful for success in college and career. For science, those content areas have been identified as life science, physical science, and Earth and space science. These areas are given different emphases on the test. GED Science Test questions will be made up of about 40% life science, 40% physical science, and 20% Earth and space science.

Additionally, you will be asked to demonstrate understanding and skill in a range of practices, or thinking skills. The test will measure how well you apply these practices to questions about written texts and visual materials, such as charts, graphs, and diagrams. Each question you see on the test will align with both a content area and a practice skill.

To help you achieve success on the GED Science Test, this book will help you review your knowledge of the content areas and practices through passages, graphics, and questions typical of those you will find on the GED test.

This book is divided into three units, each focused on one of the content areas. Every unit is made up of lessons that review specific topics and subtopics within its content area. Lessons include . . .

- Reviews of the topics and subtopics within a content area
- Graphs, charts, and diagrams of key concepts
- Definitions of important vocabulary terms
- Guided Practice pages that support you as you think through sample questions
- Hints and explanations for how to reason through the questions

After reviewing the topics, lessons, and sample questions, each unit ends with a Unit Practice, which allows you to try more questions on your own.

By studying the sample questions, you will gain an overview of the important topics that will be covered on the GED test. As you progress through the workbook, jot notes on those topics that give you the most trouble and with which you are least familiar. You will want to study these topics in greater detail as you continue your preparation for the test.

Short Answer Questions

Most of the questions in this workbook are multiple choice, but the GED test also includes other types of questions. This book includes some fill-in-the-blank questions to give you practice answering questions that are not multiple choice.

The GED Science Test includes two short answer questions. To help you prepare for these questions, this workbook also includes short answer questions to help you practice writing science answers.

In a short answer item, you will be asked to write a brief response to a science question. One of the questions may ask you to read a passage and then cite specific evidence, present a line of reasoning, or demonstrate your understanding of a science concept. The other question will test your knowledge of experimental design by asking you to identify a research question, design an investigation, or justify a line of reasoning. Here and on the GED test, you can expect these answers to take about 10 minutes to write.

If you need more practice or a better understanding of how to respond to short answer questions, you may wish to study New Readers Press's *Writing for the GED® Test*.

Unit 1: Life Science

Organization of Life

Cell Theory

scientific theory—
Theory is commonly used to mean a hunch or idea, but that is not its meaning in science. A scientific theory is a widely tested and accepted explanation of a set of observations.

The cell theory is a **scientific theory** that states that

- all living things are made up of one or more cells,
- all cells come from other cells, and
- there is no living thing smaller than a cell.

The cell is the basic unit, or building block, of life.

Organisms that have only one cell are called unicellular organisms (*unicellular* means "one-celled"). They are also called microorganisms. The bacteria that make you sick, as well as the bacteria that turn milk to yogurt, are unicellular organisms.

Organisms that have more than one cell are called multicellular organisms (*multicellular* means "many-celled"). In a multicellular organism, cells work together to make up the structures of the body and to complete the functions needed for life.

Cells Work Together

The cells in multicellular organisms work together in several ways. Some cells specialize, just as people specialize in their work as carpenters, dentists, and other professions. Some specialized cells work with other cells like them, the way that a number of carpenters may work together on a house. When a number of similar cells work together, those cells make up a tissue. An example of a tissue is your biceps.

Just as carpenters, electricians, and plumbers may work on the same building, many cells within different kinds of tissues work together in an organ. An example of an organ is the heart, where muscle tissue pumps blood and nervous tissue controls the heart rate.

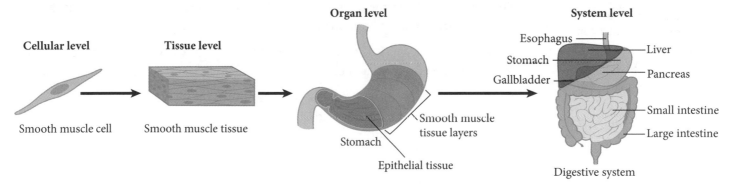

In a multicellular organism, cells are organized into a hierarchy. A familiar hierarchy is shown on this page. Letters make up words, words make up sentences, and sentences make up paragraphs. Letters are at the bottom in this hierarchy. Words are higher, and paragraphs are even higher. In cell hierarchy, cells are at the bottom. Cells make up tissues, tissues make up organs, and organs make up organ systems. The illustration shows the levels of organization in the digestive system. Muscle cells make up muscle tissue. Muscle and other tissues make up the stomach, which is an organ. The stomach and other organs make up the digestive system.

Certain things must happen for you to live. Among other things, you must get food, take in water, and get rid of wastes and toxins. This is true for you and all multicellular organisms, and it is also true for unicellular organisms. In fact, most of the things that keep an organism alive begin at the cellular level.

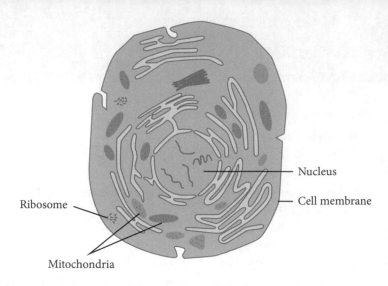

In the same way that an organism can have specialized cells, cells have specialized parts. These parts do different things to keep an organism alive.

Cell Components

ATP—adenosine triphosphate, a molecule that is the "energy currency" of the cell. It stores energy for many body processes.

chemical reaction—a change of one or more substances into one or more new substances. Energy is taken in and stored or given off during the change.

Cell membrane—Every cell has a cell membrane. The cell membrane controls how much water, sugar, sodium, and other substances flow in and out.

Chloroplasts—Chloroplasts are the cell components where photosynthesis takes place. We don't have chloroplasts, but plants do.

Mitochondria—Mitochondria package energy in a way that cells can use. Plants get energy from sunlight, and animals get energy from food. In both plants and animals, that energy is changed by mitochondria into **ATP**. Some cells, such as bacteria, don't have mitochondria.

Ribosomes—Ribosomes make enzymes. These enzymes start the chemical reactions that allow organisms to perform essential functions. Ribosomes also make proteins that are important parts of most body structures, such as bone and muscle.

Nucleus—The nucleus is the cell component that contains DNA in most types of cells. Not every type of cell has a nucleus.

Within cells, tissues, and organs, **chemical reactions** occur constantly. Chemical reactions between water, sugar, carbohydrates, proteins, lipids (fats), and other molecules allow organisms to perform the essential functions of life: metabolism, reproduction, and development.

Metabolism

Metabolism refers to all the chemical changes that occur in an organism. There are two basic functions of metabolism—breaking down and building up.

In all chemical reactions, energy is either used and stored or given off. For example, when carbohydrates are broken down, energy is given off. When proteins are built, energy is used and stored.

Chemical reactions are also how we accomplish the other essential functions of life, such as reproduction and development. They all require building materials and energy, which is why we have to eat.

All organisms need energy, and they get it from three sources: sunlight, food, and inorganic chemicals (chemicals that are not in organisms). Plants use sunlight. Animals use food. A few uncommon organisms use inorganic chemicals. (Those rare organisms have been found in isolated caves and on the ocean floor.) Most living things, though, get their energy from sunlight directly or from food. The source of the energy in food is also sunlight, so almost all organisms on Earth get their energy from the sun.

Photosynthesis

How does this happen? It starts when sunlight hits a plant or another organism that contains chloroplasts. Chloroplasts contain the green pigment called *chlorophyll*, which is what "catches" the light energy. *Photosynthesis* means "using light (*photo*) to build something (*synthesis*)." Here's the chemical reaction:

$$CO_2 \quad + \quad H_2O \quad \xrightarrow[\text{chlorophyll}]{\text{sunlight}} \quad C_6H_{12}O_6 \quad + \quad O_2$$

$$\text{Carbon dioxide} \quad + \quad \text{Water} \quad \longrightarrow \quad \text{Sugars} \quad + \quad \text{Oxygen}$$

Carbon dioxide plus water react—in the presence of light energy and chlorophyll—to produce sugars (food) and oxygen. Plants and algae use the sugars to build their body structures. For example, trees use sugars to make larger molecules (such as starch and cellulose) in order to build trunks, branches, leaves, and seeds.

Cellular Respiration

Animals get their energy by eating plant parts (such as leaves and seeds) or by eating other animals that have eaten plants, or both. Sugars and other compounds in food are broken down in chemical reactions that give off energy. When sugars are broken down in the presence of oxygen, the process is called *aerobic respiration*. The chemical reaction is basically the photosynthesis reaction in reverse:

$$C_6H_{12}O_6 \quad + \quad O_2 \quad \longrightarrow \quad CO_2 \quad + \quad H_2O \quad + \quad \text{Energy}$$

$$\text{Sugars} \quad + \quad \text{Oxygen} \quad \longrightarrow \quad \text{Carbon dioxide} \quad + \quad \text{Water} \quad + \quad \text{Energy}$$

Sugars plus oxygen react to produce carbon dioxide plus water, and energy is given off. Photosynthesis and aerobic respiration balance each other, and each makes the other possible. When plants undergo photosynthesis, they make food and give off oxygen that most animals need to live. When animals break down food, they give off carbon dioxide and water that plants need to undergo photosynthesis.

There is another type of cellular respiration—anaerobic (which means "without oxygen"). The chemical reaction still gives off energy, but not as much and not for long. This process is called *fermentation*. Unlike people, some fungi and some bacteria get much or even all of their energy through fermentation. People use fermentation by yeasts (which are fungi) to make bread dough rise.

Mitosis and meiosis are types of cell division. They are alike in many ways but have important differences, and they have very different results.

Remember that the cell theory states that all cells come from other cells. For a body cell, this happens through the process of mitosis. Before a cell divides, it makes copies of its components—more ribosomes, mitochondria, cell membrane, and DNA. The DNA molecules are on structures called *chromosomes*, so the cell makes copies of the chromosomes. Once the cell component copies are ready, the cell can "split" and become two cells with chromosomes that are exactly alike. The whole process happens in one day in some of your cells.

Mitosis

There are several phases of mitosis:

Prophase—After duplication, each chromosome looks like an X. The nucleus has enlarged to hold chromosomes that are twice the normal size.

Metaphase—The membrane around the nucleus has dissolved. Spindle fibers pull the chromosomes into the middle of the cell.

Anaphase—The two V-shaped parts (now called *chromatids*) of each chromosome are pulled apart to opposite sides of the cell.

Telophase and Cytokinesis—A new membrane begins to form around each group of chromatids, making two new nuclei. The cell membrane grows and begins to meet in the center of the cell, between the two nuclei. During cytokinesis, the two parts of the cell separate and become two cells, called *daughter cells*. Each daughter cell has a full set of chromosomes and a full array of cell components.

The time between cell divisions is called *interphase*.

   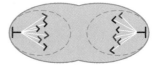

| Prophase | Metaphase | Anaphase | Telophase and Cytokinesis |

Mitosis is an important solution to a number of problems. As we live, cells get worn out or damaged. Mitosis makes new cells to replace them. New cells also allow organisms to grow and develop different structures.

Meiosis

Meiosis is another cell division process that happens in reproductive organs. Although meiosis is like mitosis in many ways, there are important differences. For one thing, meiosis has twice as many phases. Most importantly, the cells that result from meiosis have half the number of chromosomes of the parent cells. The resulting cells are **gametes**—such as egg cells in female organisms and sperm cells in males. This is true in plants as well as animals.

gamete—a mature sex cell, such as a sperm or ovum

Here are the phases of meiosis:

Prophase I—The duplicated X-shaped chromosomes move into pairs that have one chromosome each from the organism's mother and father. These are called *homologous pairs*. Next, the two chromosomes of each pair—let's call them A and B—stick together for a while in a process called *crossing over*. When they break apart, some parts of A go with B and vice versa. The result is that A is no longer an exact copy of the chromosome that came from the mother. Likewise, B is no longer identical to the chromosome that came from the father.

Metaphase I—As in mitosis, spindle fibers pull the chromosomes into the middle of the cell.

Anaphase I—The pairs split up, and one member of each pair goes to one side of the cell, while the other member of the pair goes to the other side. (Note that they do this randomly—each side gets some As and some Bs.)

Telophase I and Cytokinesis I—The cell membrane grows and meets in the center of the cell. The two parts of the cell then separate.

Prophase II—There are now two cells. Each cell has only half as many chromosomes as a body cell because there are no pairs.

Metaphase II—Spindle fibers pull the X-shaped chromosomes into the middle of the cell.

Anaphase II—As in mitosis, the two V-shaped parts of each chromosome are pulled apart to opposite sides of the cell.

Telophase II and Cytokinesis II—The two parts of the cell separate and become two cells. There are now four cells that came from one. In some organisms, these four new cells are spores that can develop into new organisms. In humans and other organisms that reproduce sexually, most of these new cells become gametes—either sperm or ova. In a man, the four cells become four sperm cells. In a woman, one of the four cells becomes an ovum.

zygote—a fertilized egg

When a sperm and ovum meet in sexual reproduction, the new cell is called a **zygote**. The zygote has a full set of chromosomes, in pairs, just like a body cell. It is a body cell at the beginning. It divides through mitosis, and its daughter cells divide through mitosis, and their daughter cells divide through mitosis and on and on. Some cells become specialized, different body structures develop, and the zygote grows into a complete organism.

Guided Practice

Sample Question   Which of the following is a correct hierarchy for the cellular levels of organization in the human body system shown?

A. gall bladder, small intestine, large intestine

B. intestinal tissue, small intestine, digestive system

C. intestinal secretory cell, intestinal connective tissue, stomach

D. large intestine, intestinal muscle cell, intestinal muscle tissue

Think It Through

Hint: Read the answer options. Eliminate the answer that shows only one level (A).

Q: What is the question asking?

A: Which choice puts the cellular levels in correct hierarchical order?

Q: How is cell hierarchy arranged?

A: Cells are at the bottom. Complex systems are at the top.

Q: Which answer choice puts related cells, tissues, organs, and systems in this order?

A: Choice A is incorrect because all three items are organs.

Choice B is correct. This is the hierarchical order of the digestive system. The order goes from cell to tissue to organ to organ system.

Choice C is incorrect because food passes through the stomach before it goes to the intestine

Choice D is incorrect because the items are not in hierarchical order.

Sample Question   Which of the following is a difference between mitosis and meiosis?

A. Mitosis does not occur in reproductive organs.

B. Mitosis only occurs in sex cells.

C. Only meiosis results in gametes.

D. Only meiosis results in zygotes.

Think It Through

Hint: Scan the terms in the answers. Which terms relate to mitosis or meiosis?

Q: What is the question asking?

A: It asks which of the choices is a *difference* between mitosis and meiosis.

Q: What happens during mitosis and meiosis?

A: Both are types of cell division.

Q: Which option is correct? Read the choices and eliminate the wrong answers.

A: Choices A and B are incorrect because mitosis occurs in all body cells, including in reproductive organs during growth and repair.

Choice C is correct because mitosis does not result in gametes.

Choice D is incorrect because neither process results in zygotes.

Genetics and Heredity

Central Dogma of Molecular Biology

DNA— deoxyribonucleic acid, the cell macromolecule that carries genetic information

There is only one way that protein can be made: Information in **DNA** is transcribed to **RNA**, and then the information is translated into protein. This is called the "central dogma of molecular biology." (*Dogma* roughly means "explanation" in this use.) This process is the mechanism of inheritance—the way organisms inherit genetic traits from their parents.

Information in DNA is coded in genes. A gene is a part of a DNA molecule, which is part of a chromosome.

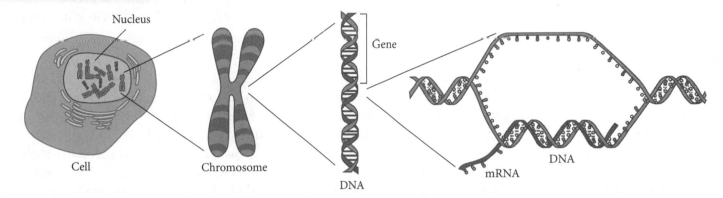

Nucleus

Cell

Chromosome

DNA

Gene

DNA

mRNA

DNA

Transcription

RNA—ribonucleic acid, a cell macromolecule that helps make protein

How is information in DNA transcribed to RNA? *Transcribe* means "write from one place to another." The DNA molecule is a double helix, which looks like a twisted zipper. It can untwist a bit at a time. Where it untwists, the "zipper teeth" come unzipped. Each type of tooth is called a base. It attracts another base of a specific type. Those bases bind together, forming just one side of a new "zipper." That's RNA, and it now has the DNA's information written on it.

The RNA leaves the DNA and slides out into the cell. (The DNA zips up and twists back into its original condition.) The RNA carries the DNA's information in code. Three bases in a row on the RNA form a codon. Each codon codes for a particular amino acid. Because the function of this type of RNA is to carry information from the DNA, it's called *messenger RNA*, or mRNA.

Translation

Proteins are made in a process called *translation*. The code carried by the messenger RNA is translated into the instructions for making proteins. Remember, the mRNA is like one half of a zipper, and three of its teeth in a row make up a codon. The mRNA moves through a ribosome the way zipper teeth move through a zipper's slider. While the ribosome holds a codon, another type of RNA (transfer RNA, or tRNA) attaches the correct amino acid to it. The amino acids bind together, forming a long chain. The chains of amino acids fold up in various ways to make proteins.

DNA from Both Parents

How does this process lead to inheritance? A sperm contains DNA. An ovum contains DNA. When an egg and sperm combine, the new organism contains DNA from both parents. The new organism's proteins are made from that combined information. Some proteins are enzymes that start the chemical reactions that allow the body to work. Other proteins are hormones—chemical messengers that tell parts of the body what to do when.

Some proteins are structural parts of muscles, bones, and membranes. Basically, proteins control the construction of every part of an organism, based on the genes it inherited from its parents.

Genetic Traits

Some species reproduce asexually and make new individuals like themselves. However, species that reproduce sexually have offspring that may or may not have the same traits as their parents. The reasons for this will be discussed in the next section. But first, let's discuss probability.

A genetic trait is something about an individual that depends on its genes. For example, the curliness (or not) of your hair is a genetic trait. How you style your hair is not. Genes code for proteins that result in genetic traits. A gene can have different alleles, or versions. An organism can inherit one allele from its mother and a different allele of that gene from its father.

Dominant and Recessive Alleles

dominant allele— the version of a gene that shows up in an organism when it also has a recessive version

As the study of genetics has progressed, we've learned that many physical traits are affected by several genes. It can be difficult to determine the influence of any particular gene in some cases. However, often there is clearly a dominant gene that influences a trait. When there is a **dominant allele**, there is also a **recessive allele**. For example, short is the dominant allele for the hair-length gene in domestic cats. Long is the recessive allele for that gene. When a cat inherits one long-hair allele and one short-hair allele, it will have short hair. That's why the short allele is called *dominant*—it wins out over the other allele.

Punnett Squares

recessive allele—the version of a gene that shows up in an organism only when it has two of the same version

Traits with dominant and recessive alleles can be predicted in offspring with the help of a Punnett square. To create a Punnett square, you need to know both alleles in both parents. Let's say you have a short-haired male cat. The short allele for hair length is dominant, so he may have either two short alleles or one short and one long allele. You know he had a long-haired mother, so that tells you that he has one long allele.

Suppose this cat mates with a long-haired female. Long hair is recessive, so she must have two long alleles. What hair length will their kittens have? Look at the Punnett square.

The Punnett square has *L* and *l* at the top to show the male's alleles. It also has *l* and *l* at the left side to show the female's alleles. The pairs of letters in the center squares show the possible alleles in their kittens. They also reveal the probability that the kittens will have the same hair length as either parent. The probability that the kittens will have short hair is 50%, because two of the four allele combinations are *Ll*. The probability that the kittens will have long hair is also 50%, because the other two allele combinations are *ll*.

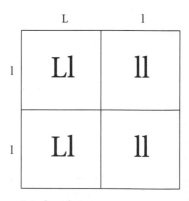

L = short hair
l = long hair

Genotypes and Phenotypes

An organism's **genotype** is the pair of alleles it has for a trait:

Heterozygous—A kitten with one of each allele for hair length (*Ll*) is heterozygous for that trait (*hetero* means "different," and *zygous* refers to the zygote—the first cell of a new organism). The Punnett square predicts that 50% of the kittens will be heterozygous.

Genetics and Heredity
New Alleles, Assortment of Alleles

> **genotype**—the combination of one or more genes for one or more traits

> **phenotype**—an organism's appearance or characteristic that results from the organism's genotype

Homozygous recessive—A kitten with two recessive alleles for hair length (*ll*) is homozygous recessive (*homo* means "same"). According to the Punnett square, 50% of the kittens will be homozygous recessive.

Homozygous dominant—A kitten with two dominant alleles for hair length (*LL*) is homozygous dominant. The Punnett square shows that these cat parents will not produce homozygous dominant kittens.

The version of a trait that an organism expresses is its **phenotype** for that trait. *Pheno* means "showing," so phenotype means "the type showing." The Punnett square predicts that 50% of the kittens will have the short-hair phenotype.

A heterozygous organism and a homozygous dominant organism will show the dominant phenotype. Only a homozygous recessive organism will have the recessive phenotype.

Pedigree Charts

Pedigree charts contain more information than Punnett squares, such as who is male and who is female. That's important in human genetics, because alleles on the female sex chromosome are more likely to show up in sons than daughters.

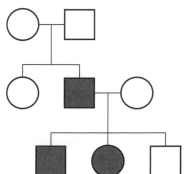

In a pedigree chart, a circle represents a female, and a square represents a male. A horizontal line between them shows that they are parents. The lines below them lead to more circles and squares, representing their children. In this pedigree chart, a woman and man are the parents of a daughter and son. The son and another woman are the parents of three children—two boys and a girl.

When the pattern of inheritance of a trait is being studied, the symbol for a person with that trait is filled in. This chart of three generations shows which family members have freckles. Neither grandparent has freckles. But their son does, and he passed that trait to his daughter and one of his sons. Pedigree charts can be used in this way to determine whether an allele is recessive or dominant. This pedigree chart shows that the presence of freckles is recessive.

New Alleles

Why are there alleles that result in freckles or long hair or other traits? Alleles come from DNA mutations. Not all mutations are bad. Many mutations lead to variety, or they have no effect at all.

Remember that DNA replicates (makes a copy of itself) before a cell divides. The DNA molecule untwists and unzips, and each of its bases attracts a complementary base. But sometimes mistakes occur. If the mistake is permanent and is present in a gene, a genetic mutation results. When this happens in a cell during meiosis, the resulting sperm or ovum has a new version of a gene—a new allele. Through sexual reproduction, that new allele gets passed on to new generations.

New Alleles, Assortment of Alleles

Assortment of Alleles

Mutations are rare and don't explain most of the differences between an organism and its parents. Variety in traits is usually due to assortment of alleles. Here are some ways in which these variations may occur:

- During prophase I in meiosis when they cross over, homologous pairs of chromosomes exchange some of their alleles.

- During anaphase I in meiosis, homologous pairs of chromosomes are pulled apart randomly into what will become separate cells. As a result, each sperm carries alleles from both of the male's parents, but not every sperm carries the same assortment. The same type of assortment happens in ova.

- Sometimes there are several possible combinations of males and females. This array of possibilities adds to the assortment of alleles, too.

After all that shuffling of alleles, an organism's genes still don't totally determine its phenotype. The way that genes are expressed will be affected by the environment. First, while a zygote or fetus is developing, it is sensitive to all the physical and chemical conditions around it. For example, fetuses can be harmed when their mothers smoke, drink alcohol, or take drugs. An organism's growth and development can also be affected by the environment. For example, a puppy may carry the genes that make it a St. Bernard, but that dog may remain smaller than expected if it doesn't get enough food.

Epigenetics

epigenetics—the study of how phenotypes change when the function, but not the structure, of genes is altered

Epigenetics is the study of how phenotypes change when the function, but not the structure, of genes is changed. One way this happens is when chemicals, such as methyl groups, attach to DNA. The same stretch of DNA (a gene) can be affected in one cell but not in another. Also, some genes but not others in the same cell can be affected. These changes can be inherited, but they can also be undone. In effect, genes are turned on and off.

Some genes are turned on and off by other environmental factors. One example is temperature, which can affect fur color in Siamese cats. The same gene in every cell of the cat's body will produce light-brown fur everywhere except on the coldest areas. That is, the "color points" of a Siamese are at the nose, ears, tail, and paws. Fur color is darker in those areas, because more pigment protein is produced in cells at lower temperatures.

Guided Practice

The GED Science Test will include two short answer items. For each of these questions, you will type your answer into a blank box.

Sample Question

Consider the information about gene expression in Siamese cats that you read on page 14. Predict the results of an experiment in which two groups of cats are kept at different temperatures for their first two years. Group A is housed at a few comfortable degrees cooler than room temperature. Group B is housed at a few comfortable degrees warmer than room temperature. What will their fur colors be, and why?

_____

_____

_____

_____

_____

_____

Think It Through

Hint: What is the effect of temperature on fur color?

Hint: When you write short answers, remember to check that you have thoroughly answered the question.

Q: What is the question asking?

A: What color fur will the cats in Group A and Group B have?

Q: What does the prompt tell you about the cats?

A: The cats in Group A are kept at a cooler temperature than the cats in Group B.

Q: What does the passage tell you about fur color in Siamese cats? Reread the passage. *Some genes are turned on and off by other environmental factors. One example is temperature, which can affect fur color in Siamese cats. The same gene in every cell of the cat's body will produce light-brown fur everywhere except on the coldest areas. That is, the "color points" of a Siamese are at the nose, ears, tail, and paws. Fur color is darker in those areas, because more pigment protein is produced in cells at lower temperatures.*

A: The skin of the cats in Group A will be cooler, so there will be more pigment protein produced in all their skin cells. Group B cats will be warmer. The cats in Group A will have darker fur than the cats in Group B.

Body Systems

Body systems are sometimes called *organ systems*. However, in addition to organs, they contain tissues and cells and work together within the complete organism—the body. So *body systems* may be a better term.

The Respiratory System

The respiratory system takes oxygen from the air into the body and expels carbon dioxide. Air enters the lungs when the diaphragm, a muscle attached to the lower ribs, contracts. This allows air to be inhaled. The air passes through the nose, throat, and trachea and enters the lungs through two bronchi. The bronchi divide into smaller passages called *bronchioles*. These end at tiny air sacs called *alveoli*. From the alveoli, oxygen passes into the blood. Carbon dioxide passes out of the blood into the alveoli. When the diaphragm relaxes, air is exhaled from the lungs, getting rid of the waste carbon dioxide.

The Circulatory System

The heart, blood vessels, and blood make up the circulatory system. A healthy human heart pumps between 60 and 100 beats per minute when the body is at rest. The blood travels through vessels. From the heart, the blood flows through arteries to smaller arteries and then to capillaries. On the way back to the heart, blood flows from capillaries to small veins and then to larger veins. The blood flows through the heart twice for each time around the body—first to the lungs and back, and then to the rest of the body and back. The capillaries have thin walls. Substances pass through the capillaries to and from the alveoli in the lungs and to and from the tissues in the rest of the body.

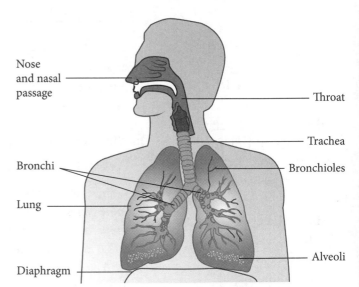

Carbon dioxide is carried by the blood from the tissues to the lungs and breathed out. What happens to other wastes? Removing them is one job of the urinary system.

The Urinary System

When blood flows to the kidneys, they filter out the waste products of metabolism. These waste products are sent through the ureters to the bladder. These wastes leave the body, in urine, through the urethra. But the urinary system only deals with liquid wastes. Removing solid wastes is part of the digestive system's function.

The Digestive System

The main job of the digestive system is to collect nutrients from food. Chewed food moves from the mouth though the esophagus and into the stomach. There, the food gets broken down more by acids. Then it goes to the small intestines, where most of the digestion and absorption of nutrients occurs. What leaves the small intestines is mostly waste. This waste goes on to the large intestines, where water is absorbed back into the body. The now-solid waste leaves the body through the rectum, which is the end of the large intestine.

The Muscular System

There are different types of muscle tissue—smooth (as in the digestive system), cardiac (in the heart), and skeletal. Skeletal tissue makes up the skeletal muscles, which move you around. They make up the major part of the muscular system. But you can't move without the skeletal system, too. The term *musculoskeletal system* is sometimes used to emphasize the combined effort.

There are about 700 skeletal muscles in the human body. Most are attached to bone at one end and to tendon at the other. Each muscle is also connected to a nerve and blood vessels.

To move part of your body, you contract one or more muscles while you relax the opposite muscle or muscles. For example, you can raise your hand, bending your arm at the elbow, by contracting your biceps muscle and relaxing your triceps on the other side of your arm.

The Skeletal System

All of the bones and their connections with ligaments and joints make up the skeletal system. Besides providing structure and protection to internal organs, bones store minerals and make red blood cells (in their marrow). In addition to working closely with the muscular system, bones protect the nervous system.

The Nervous System

The largest organ in the nervous system is the brain. It connects to the spinal cord, which contains the nerves in the spine. The nervous system sends messages from your brain to other parts of your body and vice versa. Much of the energy the body needs is used to send electrical messages throughout this system.

The Integumentary System

Skin is the body's largest organ, and it is part of your integumentary system. So are sweat and oil glands, hair, fingernails, and toenails. The main job of the integumentary system is to act as a barrier. It keeps out many pathogens, and it limits the amount of water that passes in and out.

The Lymphatic System

Sometimes called the *immune system*, the lymphatic system contains lymph nodes, the spleen, lymphocytes, and lymph vessels. The major jobs of the immune system are to fight disease and to collect fluids and return them to circulation.

The Reproductive System

The reproductive system produces sex hormones and sex cells—sperm in the two testes (male) and ova in the ovaries (female). The male system provides a method of transferring sperm. The female system provides a path for sperm to meet ova and for fertilization. The female uterus provides a protected place where a fetus can develop, and female mammary glands provide nutrition once the baby is born.

feedback mechanism— a loop system in which a signal starts a process to change a condition. In a negative feedback mechanism, the process reduces the condition. In a positive feedback mechanism, the condition is increased.

Imagine breaking an egg into a cold frying pan. The egg white will be colorless and runny. You turn on the stove. As the egg cooks, the colorless and runny part becomes white and solid. The egg white is mostly protein, and heat changes protein. All proteins are made of long chains of amino acids folded into shapes that allow them to perform different functions. The chemical bonds holding the amino acids into folded shapes break at high temperatures, and the proteins fall apart. The same thing happens to human proteins if they get too hot. What keeps that from happening is a **feedback mechanism** that maintains homeostasis. *Homeo* means "same," and *stasis* means "staying."

The human body has many homeostatic feedback mechanisms. In general, a feedback mechanism is made up of three parts: a receptor that notices a change, a control center that processes information sent by the receptor, and an effector that follows instructions from the control center. Two examples follow.

Overheating

If you get too hot, receptors sense the change and feed this information to your control center (the brain). Two things happen: You sweat, and your blood flow changes so that more blood flows through the vessels near your skin. The result is that heat moves from the body to the air. When the receptors sense that your body temperature has returned to normal, they send that new information back to the control center. Your blood flow returns to normal, and you stop sweating.

A typical home-heating system has a similar feedback mechanism. The thermostat is the receptor and control center combined. If the home gets too cold, the thermostat senses the change and turns on the heater (the effector). The result is that the home warms up. When the thermostat senses that the temperature has returned to normal, it turns off the heater.

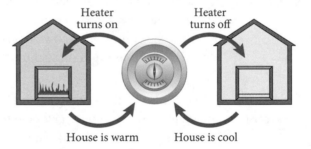

Heater turns on   Heater turns off

House is warm   House is cool

Hypothermia

If your body gets too cold, receptors sense it and signal the control center. At this point, the control center sends out signals to begin warming behaviors. People often respond by putting on more clothes, getting out of the wind, or turning up a heater. However, if receptors continue sensing that the body is cold, they keep signaling the control center. The control center then sends out instructions for physical responses. Muscles shiver, which generates body heat. Blood flows away from the skin, which prevents heat loss to the air and sends warm blood to the most important body parts—the heart and brain. When the receptors sense that your body temperature has returned to normal, they signal the control center with the new information. As a result, your blood flow returns to normal and you stop shivering.

Sources of Nutrients

nutrients—substances that provide nourishment for the essential functions of life

We get **nutrients** from food. How do our bodies transform nutrients into materials we can use?

1. The digestive system breaks food down into small molecules.

2. Those small molecules are absorbed from the digestive system into the blood.

3. The blood carries the small molecules to cells, which pull them through the cell membrane if they are needed.

4. Some of the small molecules are combined to make macromolecules (proteins, carbohydrates, lipids, and nucleic acids) and other structures needed in the cells at that time. Other small molecules (such as sugars) are broken down to give off energy.

Did you know that most of the cells in a person are actually not human cells? We play host to many helpful bacteria. Lactobacilli and bifidobacteria, which live in our intestines, help us digest food. *Lactobacillus acidophilus* is so helpful that people purposely eat foods, such as yogurt, that contain it.

Your nutritional requirements include many things:

Calories

The calorie is a measure of how much energy is in food. We don't all need the same number of calories. Growth, pregnancy, and exercise increase the number of calories a person needs. Basically, if you're losing weight (and don't want to), you need more calories. If you're gaining weight (and don't want to), you need fewer calories.

Water

Pure water is not a food, but you can't digest your food—or do anything else—unless you get enough water. Eight 8-ounce glasses of water per day is a general guideline. You may need more if you've been been sweating. How much plain water you need also depends on what else you drink and even what you eat. Some foods, such as celery, contain a lot of water.

Carbohydrates

Starch and other food carbohydrates are broken down into sugars. These sugars are used for energy or broken down to atoms of carbon, hydrogen, and oxygen. Your body uses those atoms to build the small molecules that are then used to build larger molecules, like DNA and proteins.

Fats

Fats provide us with vitamins and important fatty acids such as omega-3 and omega-6. Generally, unsaturated fats (in nuts and olive oil) are healthier than saturated fats (in butter, beef, and chicken skin). Omega-6 fatty acid is easy to get from corn oil, and anchovies and walnuts are good sources of omega-3.

Vitamins and Minerals

Vitamins are organic substances that are essential for good health. Citrus fruits like oranges are popular sources of vitamin C. The B vitamins are available from many foods. Minerals are essential for good health, like vitamins. But minerals are inorganic substances such as iron, sodium, potassium, calcium, magnesium, and zinc. The best way to get all the minerals you need is to eat a wide variety of foods.

Some diseases, such as heart disease, asthma, and diabetes, are not communicable. Other diseases are communicable, or contagious. They can be spread from person to person. This spread is called *disease transmission*.

What is actually spread is a pathogen, usually a bacterium or virus. There are many ways for this to happen, including

- the fecal-oral route (for example, with salmonella food poisoning and cholera),
- direct contact with blood (as with HIV and hepatitis B and C), and
- direct or indirect contact with saliva or mucus (as with the common cold and the flu).

Transmission by the fecal-oral route is the main reason we are all taught to wash our hands after using the toilet. It has been partly controlled by sewer systems in many parts of the world and by proper food handling.

Transmission of blood-borne diseases between people can be prevented if two precautions are taken: the careful control of blood and associated body fluids of infected people and the protection of the tissues of others.

Airborne Transmission

Many common communicable diseases are transmitted in saliva or mucus. Often, the pathogens leave an infected person and become airborne. Quite frequently they land on objects that will soon be touched by other people: telephones, doorknobs, clothes, or the ground. Of course, these pathogens get an extra boost if the saliva or mucus goes right from one person to another. Common and effective preventive actions include washing your hands frequently, especially before putting them near your face. If you're sick with an airborne pathogen, you should stay away from other people and be very careful with your mucus and saliva—cover your sneezes and coughs, and wash your own hands frequently, too.

Airborne diseases such as the flu can move from one person to another, and from one geographic area to another, very quickly. The flu is not always a serious disease, but it can be. The Centers for Disease Control and Prevention (CDC) has estimated that deaths associated with flu have ranged from about 3,000 to 49,000 people per year in this country recently. About 69,800 people died from flu in the United States in the winter of 1957–58. In the widespread flu of 1918–19, 50 million people died worldwide. Because of the potential for danger, government and news agencies send out alerts during flu season, giving updates on the states and cities that have reported cases. They also send out reminders that people should consider getting flu shots.

Vaccines

A flu shot is a vaccine, which is a bit of pathogen that is usually dead or weakened. The goal of a vaccine is to help the organism develop an immunity to the pathogen in order to to prevent illness. Flu viruses mutate, or change, over time, so the vaccine must be remade every year. Other vaccines, such as those for measles, mumps, and rubella, are effective for many years. Vaccines have been very successful in preventing transmission of many diseases, including tuberculosis and polio, which were once widespread but are uncommon now.

Guided Practice

Sample Question

The lymphatic system contains a series of tubes that run throughout the body. These tubes collect excess fluid from body tissues and return it to the blood. Which other body system is the lymphatic system most similar to?

A. the respiratory system

B. the circulatory system

C. the digestive system

D. the skeletal system

Think It Through

Hint: Read each answer choice.

Q: What is the question asking?

A: It asks which body system is like the lymphatic system.

Q: What does the lymphatic system do?

A: The lymphatic system collects fluid from the body and returns it to the blood.

Q: Which system performs a similar function?

Choices A and C are incorrect because the digestive and respiratory systems do not run throughout the body.

Choice B is correct because the circulatory system also collects and circulates substances from body tissues.

Choice D is incorrect because the skeletal system does not have tubes.

Sample Question

Omega-3 and omega-6 are two kinds of _____, which are important building blocks of the fats and oils in the foods we eat.

Think It Through

Hint: What healthy nutrient do we get from unsaturated fats?

Q: What is the question asking?

A: It asks what omega-3 and omega-6 are.

Q: What does the question tell you about them?

A: It says that they are "important building blocks in fats and oils."

Answer: fatty acids

Common Ancestry

evolution—the
development of new
types of organisms from
preexisting types of
organisms over time

In 1859, Charles Darwin wrote *On the Origin of Species by Means of Natural Selection*. This book and others began the widespread study of **evolution**—the development of new organisms over time. The theory of evolution doesn't explain why there is life on Earth or how life began. Instead, it explains why there are so many species and how they came from other species.

One part of the theory of evolution is that all species have a common ancestry. We know that all organisms are made of cells. Each cell contains DNA. The DNA in every cell is made of the same molecules and has the same structure. Different species have many similar DNA sequences. This supports the idea that all organisms have a common ancestor.

Amino-Acid Sequences

DNA carries the information needed to create proteins. Proteins are long chains of amino acids. A study of proteins in different species has shown that many amino-acid sequences are the same. For example, many species have amino-acid sequences that make up the protein hemoglobin (which carries oxygen in the blood). However, the amino-acid sequences that make up hemoglobin in bears, for example, are different from those for hemoglobin in mice. The similarities support the idea that all species are related. The differences support the idea that species evolve—that their genetic traits change over time.

Similar Cell Structures and Processes

The cells of all species have a cell membrane. The cells of all eukaryotic species have a nucleus and other cell organelles. In all species, these cell components perform the same functions. These similarities support the idea that all species are related.

Comparison of Traits

Comparative anatomy is the comparison of analogous structures, homologous structures, and vestigial structures in different species.

Analogous Structures

Analogous structures are body parts that are similar in species but that didn't develop in the same way. For example, flying insects and birds have wings, but the structures didn't develop the same way. Bird wings include bones that look like finger and arm bones. Fly wings have no bones. These analogous structures don't show a relationship between species.

Homologous Structures

Common ancestry is shown, though, in homologous structures—body parts that developed in similar ways but have different functions. As mentioned, bird wings have bones similar to our finger and arm bones. Birds use wings to fly, which we cannot do. We use our arms and hands to hold things, which birds cannot do with their wings. Homologous structures like these support the idea of common ancestry.

Vestigial Structures

Vestigial structures are body parts that a species has but doesn't use. Examples include the human appendix, ear muscles, and the coccyx (tailbone). Whales have pelvic (hip) bones. Kiwis, which are flightless birds, have 2-inch wings. Vestigial structures like these support the idea that species evolved from ancestors that used the complete structures.

Fossil Record

There are also clues to our common ancestry in the fossil record. The age of a fossil can be determined through carbon-14 dating. The ages of fossils underground can also be determined from the type of rock they're in. In addition, their relation to each other can often be told from where the fossils are found. Suppose a bird fossil is found higher in the side of a rock canyon than a lizard fossil—that is, in a younger layer of rock. We can tell from their positions that the bird lived more recently than the lizard. We can also examine the fossils for homologous structures. The fossil record supports the idea that species have evolved for millions of years from common ancestors.

Cladograms

Cladograms are diagrams that show the similarities between different organisms. You can build a cladogram by following these steps:

1. Compare and contrast the traits of a number of different species.
2. Organize the species according to their similar traits. You can use concentric circles to do this.
3. Place the species and their traits on a branching diagram.

For a group of species made up of tuna, bullfrogs, iguanas, wolves, and domestic cats, the circles would look like this:

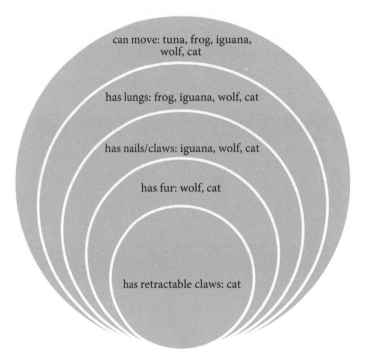

can move: tuna, frog, iguana, wolf, cat

has lungs: frog, iguana, wolf, cat

has nails/claws: iguana, wolf, cat

has fur: wolf, cat

has retractable claws: cat

All of these organisms move, so they are all in the outer circle. Tuna have gills, but the other species have lungs and are in the next smaller circle. All but the bullfrogs have claws or nails, in the even smaller circle. Only wolves and cats have fur, and wolves can't retract (pull in) their claws, so only cats make it to the smallest circle.

When you put the species and their traits on a cladogram, it looks like this:

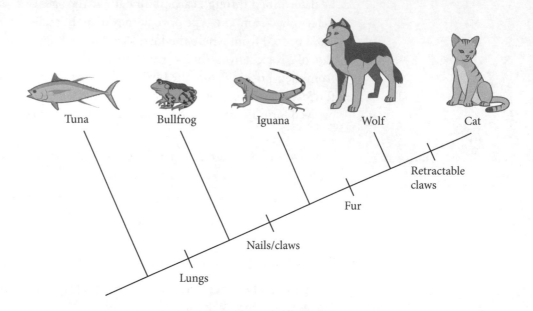

Cladograms don't tell the whole evolutionary story. For one thing, they are based on phenotypic (showing) traits, not on DNA. Also, they don't show the relationships between ancestors and descendants. However, cladograms can be helpful in studying how different species may have evolved from others.

natural selection—
the process by which individuals that are better suited to their environment survive and reproduce more successfully than less well-suited individuals do

In his theory of **natural selection,** Darwin proposed: (1) Most species have more offspring than needed to maintain their population. Each pair of mice, for example, produces dozens of offspring. (2) Resources are limited, so individuals must compete for them. In the case of the mice, there is not enough food to allow all to survive. (3) In every population, there are variations in traits. Some individuals have traits that allow them to thrive and reproduce, passing their traits to offspring. Other individuals have less useful traits. They may not survive to reproduce, or they may reproduce fewer offspring. The mice that are strong, able to find food, and successful at mating will pass on their traits. This process is called natural selection.

Evidence for Natural Selection

Scientists have studied species that have adapted to new environments. They found a high correlation between the ecological divergence of more than 500 species and their reproductive isolation. What does that mean?

- Scientists have found a correlation—two or more things are related. High correlation means that the relationship is seen often.

- The ecological divergence observed included changes in what each species eats, its size, and its habitat. Some members of the species were able to change what they ate or where they lived, or their sizes changed, because of variation in traits. That is, some members of the species were able to live under new conditions. Those members lived and reproduced, and their helpful traits were passed on. Over time, they become different from their ancestors.

- When a group is reproductively isolated, members of the group can only reproduce with other members of the group. They may mate with members of other groups, but they will not produce healthy offspring. Reproductive isolation defines *species* as a group that reproduces with others in the group.

So, this high correlation between ecological divergence and reproductive isolation supports Darwin's idea. That is, new species come from changes in old species, and all organisms have a common ancestry.

Artificial Selection

The concept of variation in genetic traits had been understood for centuries. Breeding animals and plants to express better alleles is called *artificial* selection. It is not *natural* selection, because it doesn't occur naturally. Artificial selection is performed by people, usually in farm animals, pets, and plants. But in both types of selection, the process depends on variation of alleles and occurs over generations.

An example of artificial selection can be found in corn. Maize, the ancestor of corn, had heads about the length of your thumb, each with 50 small kernels. But some maize plants had bigger heads. Some also had more kernels per head. Others had bigger kernels. By careful hand-pollination, people produced maize plants that had more favorable alleles. They kept breeding these plants, and eventually corn was a much better crop plant than maize had been. It had heads the length of a person's hand and lots of big kernels.

speciation—the formation of a new species in the course of evolution

Adaptation, like selection and evolution in general, is an ongoing process. It happens slowly over a number of generations. When adaptation to changed conditions doesn't happen quickly enough, a species may go extinct. When adaptation does happen, it may result in the evolution of a new species. This is how **speciation** works.

Individuals have genes, which are portions of the DNA in their cells. In species that reproduce sexually, each individual has two genes of each kind—one from each parent. Some of those genes are expressed as traits (such as fur color). Some of the genes are not expressed, but they are still carried. They can still be passed on to offspring.

Populations

population—all the members of a species in one place at one time

When a group of individuals of a species are in one place at one time, they make up a **population**. That population includes many individuals that have the same set of genes. For example, one set of genes makes cheetahs be cheetahs, while a different set of genes makes lions be lions. What's important here is that individuals in a population have different varieties (alleles) of the genes for their species. So in that population, there is variation of traits (such as fur color differences).

If there's not much change in the lives of this population, their pool of genes may not change much either. However, if the conditions change—for example, if the group gets so big that there's not enough food to go around—the gene pool will start changing, too. In this example, the individuals with the traits that help them get food, such as the ability to climb to reach food or to push others away from the food, will survive better than others. This is sometimes called *differential survival* or *survival of the fittest*.

Those that survive and attract mates will produce offspring. Those that don't survive, aren't healthy, or can't attract mates won't produce offspring and pass on their genes. As a result, their traits will become less common in the gene pool of the population. This is the process of natural selection. The conditions that cause it are called *selective pressures*.

Selective Pressures

Selective pressures are any conditions that cause a population to change. They can include natural disasters such as hurricanes or earthquakes. Hurricanes often blow away or flood natural shelters and food. Earthquakes can physically divide one area into two, making it harder for animals to migrate or find mates. Human-caused disasters have similar results. For example, oil spills in wetlands coat the plants, used as natural shelters, with toxic chemicals. Oil may cover and poison food. Human development in cities and suburbs can divide areas, making migration or mate searches difficult. Climate change—natural or human-caused—can pressures populations to move into areas that have a climate to which they are more accustomed. Some populations stay where they have been and adjust to the new temperatures and the amount of water that's available. Some won't be able to adjust fast enough or move to better areas, and they will die out.

As a result of differential survival for any reason, a population will have a different combination of traits than its ancestors did. This adjustment over time to different conditions is called *adaptation*. One result of adaptation can be speciation. That is, the population will become a new species.

The Galápagos finches are a good example of how adaptation can result in new species. These finches live on the Galápagos Islands off the coast of Ecuador in South America. More than a million years ago, their ancestors lived on the mainland, which is about 960 kilometers (about 600 miles) away. They may have been blown to the island by a strong storm. In any case, once the ancestral birds reached the island, some of the conditions were different from what they had been used to. For one thing, the food sources were different. In fact, over the years that the finches have been on the islands, droughts and heavy rainfall have changed the food sources several more times.

The finches had the same set of genes, but they had different alleles and therefore slightly different traits. Different traits helped them get different foods, and the finches began to specialize. Their ancestors were seed eaters with strong beaks, and the birds with larger and stronger beaks could eat larger and harder seeds than some others could. Some finches could eat smaller seeds more easily with their smaller beaks. And some finches with longer and thinner beaks could catch and eat more insects. Finches that found enough food of some kind survived, reproduced, and passed down the traits that helped them find food.

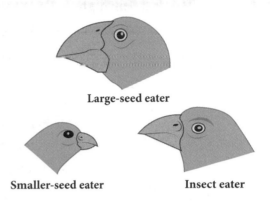

Large-seed eater

Smaller-seed eater　　　**Insect eater**

As you would expect, these better food-finding traits became more common than the traits of the ancestors. In one group of finches, the allele for large and strong beaks became very common. In another group, the allele for small beaks became very common. In a third group, the long-and-thin allele became very common.

After several generations, the groups were different enough that they didn't breed with each other anymore—they had become new species. Over the years, there have been at least 14 finch species on the Galápagos Islands. They all came from one species of ancestors.

Guided Practice

Sample Question   What is natural selection?

A. the competition among individuals of a species for environmental resources

B. the development of species over time from the original single-celled organisms

C. the result of better reproductive success among individuals with more helpful traits

D. the development of different species as a result of migration and geographic isolation

Think It Through   **Q:** What is the question asking?

A: It asks what natural selection is.

Q: What is the result of the process of natural selection?

A: The result of natural selection is the survival of species which are best suited to their environment.

Choice A is incorrect because it describes only a small part of what natural selection is about.

Choice B is incorrect. It describes evolution in general.

Choice C is correct because it describes natural selection. It is the mechanism for evolution that involves variation in traits and the greater survival and reproduction of individuals with more helpful traits, with the result that those traits become more common in the generations that follow.

Choice D is incorrect because it describes adaptation.

Sample Question   Comparative anatomy involves examining structures of organisms. Which type of structure is described correctly?

A. Analytical structures are parts that separate one group of organisms from others in a cladogram.

B. Analogous structures are used differently in different species but developed in similar ways.

C. Homologous structures are similar parts that developed differently in different species.

D. Vestigial structures are body parts that a species has but doesn't seem to use.

Think It Through   **Q:** What is the question asking?

A: Which description of a structure is correct?

Choice A is incorrect. *Analytical structures* is not a term used in comparative anatomy.

> **Hint:** Read each answer choice. Eliminate the incorrect descriptions.

Choice B and choice C are incorrect because the explanations for analogous and homologous structures are switched. Analogous structures are similar parts that developed differently in different species. Homologous structures are used differently in different species but developed in similar ways.

Choice D is correct. Vestigial structures are body parts that a species has but doesn't seem to use, such as the human appendix or tailbone.

Ecosystems

Flow of Energy in Ecosystems

ecosystem—a community of living and nonliving things and the interactions among them

We hear the word *environment* a lot. We also hear the word *ecosystem*. These terms are related but have different meanings. *Environment* generally means "surroundings." The environment includes living things (such as people, animals, plants, and bacteria) and also nonliving things (such as water and rocks).

An **ecosystem** also includes both living and nonliving things, but the term is used to stress how those things interact. There are many types of ecosystems (such as forest, grassland, and aquatic). The living and nonliving things are different in different ecosystems, but the interactions are the same. And energy plays a large part in these interactions.

Energy Pyramids

The ultimate source of almost all energy on Earth is the sun. The sun's energy is captured by plants and other photosynthetic organisms. They tie up the sun's energy in sugars. From that point, energy flows though the living things as one organism eats another. However, not all of the energy in an organism stays there after its meal. Some energy is lost to the environment—as body heat or in moving around. This loss of energy happens every time an organism eats another organism. The flow of energy through an ecosystem is often represented by an energy pyramid.

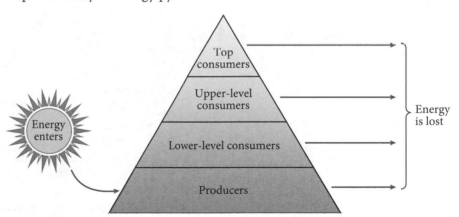

Consider the African savannah. The producers are mostly grasses, bushes, and trees. The energy in the producers flows into the lower-level consumers when they eat plants. Lower-level consumers include zebras, antelopes, wildebeests, giraffes, and elephants. Notice that these are not small animals. But the savannah has a lot of plants. There is more energy stored in all the plants than in the lower-level consumers.

The upper-level consumers on the savannah include cheetahs, hyenas, leopards, and lions. They eat zebra, antelopes, and wildebeests. As in the previous level, there are a lot more herbivores than carnivores.

The next level, the top consumers, varies. The same species that are upper-level consumers may be top consumers at times. Lions and leopards eat cheetahs, and hyenas eat almost anything. Whatever the top consumer is, it will lose energy from its meal. Much of it will be lost in the hunt.

Energy flows though an ecosystem as matter. The flow of matter can be shown in a diagram of a food web. A food web, like a spider web, is made up of a number of chains that interact. These are food chains—sequences of what eats what. You can diagram a food chain by using species names and arrows and remembering one important rule: the arrow points from the food to the species that eats it. It's as if the arrow is pointing to the mouth that is next in line.

Consider the boreal (coniferous) forest ecosystem. In a boreal forest, forbs are producers. Forbs are small plants with broad leaves, such as dandelions or clover. Parts of these forbs are eaten by chipmunks, which are eaten by goshawks, which are eaten by great horned owls. That food chain diagram looks like this:

Forbs → Chipmunks → Goshawks → Great horned owls

A decomposer is a type of organism that gets energy from breaking down waste matter. Typical decomposers are bacteria and fungi (such as mushrooms). Decomposers are not usually shown in energy pyramids. However, they are shown in food chains, as you can see here:

Grasses → Fungi → Red squirrels → Red-tailed hawks → Great horned owls

Food Webs   If you combine a number of food chains in one diagram, you have a diagram of a food web. You can see that this food web includes the food chains above, plus others.

Boreal Forest Food Web

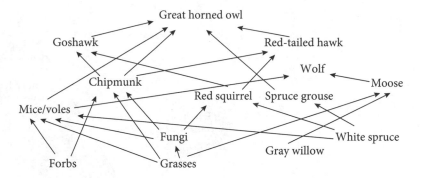

This diagram actually shows only a few of the species that interact in a boreal forest ecosystem. A healthy food web is complex, which makes it strong. If food chains weren't connected, then a break in one link of the chain would doom all the organisms beyond that link. The more food chains there are connected in a food web, the more food options there are—if a link breaks, there's something else to eat.

As with any ecosystem, there are few top consumers but many producers in a boreal forest ecosystem. Although the decomposers are shown only once, they affect every species in a food web. Wastes (such as animal feces and fallen leaves) and the remains of dead organisms are broken down by bacteria and fungi. Thus, more energy is stored in those decomposers, and less is lost to the environment. The process also recycles matter—carbon and other atoms and molecules—which become part of the soil or water. From there, they are used by the producers and reenter the food web.

Carrying Capacity

carrying capacity—the largest population that an environment can support at any given time

Every ecosystem has a **carrying capacity** for each species. The carrying capacity is the number of individuals of a species (the size of a population) that can live in an ecosystem. If there are more, the ecosystem won't function properly. That is, the interactions of the organisms in it will change, so the system itself will change.

Limiting Resources

Carrying capacity depends on these limiting resources:

Air—As any scuba diver knows, air is the number-one limiting resource. Air contains the oxygen that people and animals need and the carbon dioxide that plants need. In aquatic and marine ecosystems, fish and algae get oxygen and carbon dioxide that are dissolved in the water.

Water—After air, fresh water is the most limiting natural resource. Cells, and eventually organisms, die without enough water. For animals, it's important that the water is clean and free of pathogens, parasites, and toxins. Most plants get their water from the soil. Marine organisms need clean and healthy salt water.

Food—Plants combine carbon dioxide and water, in the presence of sunlight, to make food. They use that food for their essential functions, just as we do. Animals eat the food (sugars) that the plants have made, as well as other matter in the plants. Some animals can't last more than a day without eating. People and some other animals can go a few days without eating, but we all need to eat to live.

Shelter from the Elements—Shelled animals, such as turtles and snails, carry their shelters with them. But animals must maintain livable body temperatures, and even turtles need more than shells for that. A wet animal loses a lot of body heat. Cold temperatures are also easier to live through in a wind-proof shelter (wind blows away body heat). Insulation, such as piles of dry leaves, makes a shelter even more helpful. Even plants need shelter—for example, shade-loving plants need shelter from the sun.

Protection from Predators—Predators (organisms that eat other organisms) come in all shapes and sizes, and so do the means of protection from predators. Ants need protection from birds and spiders. Some ant species protect themselves by living inside plants that have thorns. Bank swallows, armadillos, and rattlesnakes all use holes in the earth to protect themselves. Herd animals find safety in numbers. Some herd animals form protective circles around their young. Others give their predators a harder time by running; it's harder to catch one zebra when a running herd looks like many moving stripes.

Space—Animals need space for activities such as finding mates, raising offspring, and collecting food. Different animal species have different space requirements. For example, emperor penguins stand shoulder to shoulder for much of the year. On the other hand, cougars defend territory within a range of 40–90 square kilometers.

Fluctuation

Limiting resources determine the number of each species an ecosystem can support, but populations don't stay the same. A population grows as new individuals move into an area or offspring are born. Conversely, a population shrinks when individuals move out or die. In a balanced ecosystem, a graph of population over time will look like this:

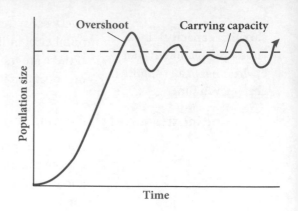

Pressures on populations and their carrying capacities include loss of resources and competition for resources. For example, if part of a boreal forest is logged, the ecosystem will provide less space, shelter, and producers. Less white spruce will mean less food for mice. This will decrease the carrying capacity for mice, which may also decrease the carrying capacities for great horned owls and wolves, which compete for mice.

Predation

Limiting resources affect the populations within ecosystems, but so do the many kinds of interspecies relationships. One important relationship is between predators and prey.

Sometimes in the boreal forest, moose are hard for wolves to find. Then, wolves depend more on mice. Mice are quick at reproducing. However, if wolves eat too many mice too quickly, there may not be enough adult mice to keep the population high. If the mouse population drops, the wolf population will drop soon after, for lack of food. If neither population dies out, the remaining mice will reproduce. More will survive—because there will be fewer wolves to eat them—so the mouse population will increase. That will make more food for the wolves, so the wolf population will rise again, as well. Eventually, the wolves may eat so many mice that the cycle will repeat.

This up-and-down cycle is less likely when there are more prey animals involved. For example, another mouse predator is the great-horned owl. The boreal forest food web shown previously indicates that these owls also eat goshawks, chipmunks, spruce grouse, and red-tailed hawks. Because there are many food options, even if the mouse population drops, the owl population will probably not be affected.

Symbiosis

Ecological symbiosis is a very close relationship between two species. Symbiotic relationships include the following:

symbiosis—a relationship in which two different organisms live in close association with each other

Parasitism—A parasite is an organism that lives on or in an organism of another species (the host) and gets food, or some other resource, from the host. For example, a flea is a parasite that gets its food from the animal it lives on. In parasitism, the host is harmed.

Commensalism—A commensal organism gets food or another resource from an organism of another species, but the other species is not harmed. It is not helped, either. An example is a bluebird nesting in a hole in a tree.

Mutualism—When an organism of one species lives in or on an organism of another species and both are helped, they have a mutualistic relationship. For example, when an oxpecker (a bird) gets it food (ticks) from an ox, both organisms benefit.

Disruption of Ecosystems

biodiversity—biological diversity, which is a combination of (1) the number of organisms in a species and (2) the number of different species

Ecosystems maintain a balance—similar to homeostasis in the human body. They can be pushed off balance and recover after small pushes. Larger pressures can change ecosystems completely. When that happens, some of their organisms won't get enough of the limiting resources discussed previously. Some populations will decrease as members move away or die out. As a result, **biodiversity**—a measure of an ecosystem's balance and health—will decrease.

Causes of Disruption

Some of the pressures that disrupt ecosystems are due to human activity, and some are natural events:

Alien species are species that come into an ecosystem from somewhere else. Many go unnoticed. However, some (such as emerald ash borers) kill native organisms (ash trees). Others (such as zebra mussels) outcompete native organisms and overpopulate. Alien species that harm an ecosystem are called *invasive species.*

Overpopulation isn't just caused by alien species. Native populations can get too big when nothing keeps them in balance. In many ecosystems, white-tailed deer populations damage plants because their natural predators (wolves and cougars) have been removed.

Fire and flood have immediate and long-term effects. Organisms that can't escape—plants and slow-moving animals that can't fly or swim—are killed. The destruction of food (plants and animals) and natural shelters are lasting changes.

Habitat destruction is the wrecking of an area's surroundings and resources. One example is deforestation. Another is desertification—the overuse of land ecosystems to the point that the soil no longer contains water or nutrients. Pollution also destroys habitats.

Climate change is a pressure affecting ecosystems now. While climate conditions do cycle naturally, human-caused climate change may be pushing ecosystems off balance. Results include widespread changes in temperature, reduced water availability, and stronger storms.

Extinction

Where there is ecosystem disruption and reduced biodiversity, food webs become simpler and easier to damage. The system may fall apart. The good news is that different species will take over the area, and a new ecosystem will develop there. The bad news is that the species that used to live there will be gone. Species that have populations in other places will be called extirpated from the area. Those that don't will be extinct. Cheetahs are a good example of the difference. Cheetahs were once found in Africa, the Middle East, and India. They have been extirpated from all but a few areas in Africa and Iran. People have been working to prevent their extinction.

Why does it matter if a few species become extinct or are extirpated from an ecosystem? Extinction is a red flag. It indicates that biodiversity is decreasing—that ecosystems are out of balance.

Conservation biology is a growing field of science. It applies knowledge of ecology, land use planning, and many other things to the goal of maintaining biodiversity. Its most far-reaching concept: In order to maintain Earth's ability to support us, we must protect its ecosystems.

Guided Practice

Sample Question   Examples of lower-level consumers include buffalo and rabbits. What is the characteristic that is common to all lower-level consumers? _____

Think It Through

> **Hint:** What do buffalo and rabbits have in common?

Q: What is the question asking?

A: It asks what lower-level consumers, such as buffalo and rabbits, have in common.

Q: What do you know about lower-level consumers?

A: They eat plants.

Answer: They eat plants (or producers).

Sample Question

Examples of Interspecies Relationships

	Species A	Action of Species A	Species B	Effect on Species B
1	*Toxocara cati*	Gets nutrients from intestines of Species B	*Felis catus*	Loses weight, may have diarrhea
2	*Felis rufus*	Takes food from Species B	*Felis lynx*	Finds new territory or goes hungry
3	*Felis lynx*	Catches and eats Species B	*Lepus americanus*	Dies
4	*Tillandsia usneoides*	Gets minerals and support from Species B	*Quercus virginiana*	None

According to the table, which relationship is an example of parasitism?

A. 1

B. 2

C. 3

D. 4

Think It Through

> **Hint:** Read across each row to see what effect the action of Species A has on Species B.

Q: What is the question asking?

A: Which interspecies relationship shown on the chart demonstrates parasitism?

Q: What is parasitism?

A: A parasite lives on or in another organism that is harmed in the relationship.

Choice A is correct. Row 1 describes the relationship between Species A (feline roundworm) and Species B (cat). In this case, Species A feeds on Species B, and Species B loses weight and has diarrhea.

Choices 2 and three are incorrect. Species A in both scenarios does not live on or in Species B.

Choice 4 is incorrect because Species A has no effect on Species B.

Guided Practice

Sample Question

Researchers developing a new virus vaccine performed several clinical trials with human volunteers. In each trial, one group of 100 volunteers received an injection of the vaccine. Another group of 100 volunteers received an injection of harmless saline. Over the first seven clinical trials, those who got the vaccine showed fewer virus symptoms, on average, than the people who got saline. The ratios of sick people in the vaccine versus saline groups were 5/15, 3/18, 7/5, 4/7, 16/20, 1/3, and 6/11.

Among those who received the vaccine, what was the mean number of people who showed virus symptoms?

A. 6

B. 5

C. 0.05

D. 5%

Think It Through

Hint: *Mean* is the same as *average*.

Q: What is the question asking?

A: It asks for the mean number of people in the vaccine group who were sick.

Q: How do you calculate the mean?

A: Add the number of sick people in the vaccine groups: 5 + 3 + 7 + 4 + 16 + 1 + 6 = 42. Then divide the total by the number of groups: 42 ÷ 7 = 6.

Choice A is correct.

Sample Question

Explain why some of the volunteers received saline rather than the vaccine.

_____

_____

_____

_____

Think It Through

Hint: What is a control group? How is a control group used in an experiment?

Q: What is the question asking?

A: Why did some people get saline shots instead of the vaccine?

Q: How was the experiment designed? Reread the passage at the top of the page.

A: The experiment tested a new vaccine. To see if the vaccine worked, one group received the vaccine, and the other group received saline shots. Those who got saline made up the control group. The control group was used to compare the number of people who got sick without the vaccine to the number who got sick with the vaccine. A control group in an experiment shows whether the results were due to the variable being tested or just chance.

1. Which of these is a correct description of cellular function in the human body?

   A. Mitochondria build proteins.

   B. The nucleus packages energy as ATP.

   C. Cell membranes control water flow.

   D. Chloroplasts use sunlight to make food.

2. The HIV virus has a diameter of about 0.1 micrometer. It is covered by a lipid membrane that is similar to the lipid-protein cell membrane. The virus does not have DNA but has RNA that contains its genes. The virus must infect a cell in order to make copies of itself. A prokaryotic cell is the smallest type of cell. It has a diameter of about 2 to 5 micrometers. A prokaryotic cell is covered by a lipid-protein cell membrane and has DNA that contains its genes. A prokaryotic cell can make copies of itself. Based on this information, explain why there is a debate about whether viruses are living things.

   _____

   _____

   _____

   _____

   _____

   _____

   _____

   _____

3. The substances in cells are built up and broken down during development and metabolism. These processes are examples of

   _____

4. Which cellular process is the basis for the manufacture of yogurt?

   A. reproduction

   B. photosynthesis

   C. aerobic respiration

   D. anaerobic respiration

5. How would a switch from aerobic respiration to anaerobic respiration help a zebra that is being chased by a lion?

   _____

   _____

   _____

   _____

   _____

6. At the end of meiosis in either sex, there are four cells called _____ that have come from one cell. In a male, the cell contains 46 chromosomes before meiosis, and each sperm contains _____ chromosomes.

7. Which of the following is a type of ecological symbiosis?

   A. parasitism

   B. competition

   C. consumption

   D. species invasion

Questions 8 and 9 refer to the following diagram.

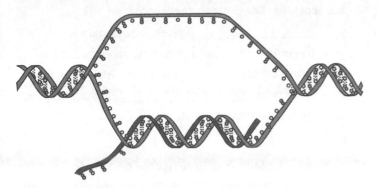

8. What molecule is being created where the helix is unzipping?

   A. DNA

   B. codon

   C. protein

   D. RNA

9. Compare and contrast the structure and function of RNA with the structure and function of DNA shown in the figure.

   _____

   _____

   _____

   _____

   _____

10. If there are four alleles—a, b, c, and d—for a gene, and a is the allele for the dominant trait, what are the permutations for the genotype of an individual displaying that trait?

    A. aa

    B. ab, ba

    C. ba, ca, da

    D. aa, ab, ac, ad

Questions 11 and 12 refer to the following scenario and Punnett squares.

	G	G
g		
g		

	G	g
g		
g		

Assume that scientists have identified the gene that determines color in a species of lizard. The dominant allele (G) is for green scales. The recessive allele (g) is for gray scales. The two possible ways to prepare Punnett squares for the mating of a green and a gray lizard are shown.

11. The genotypes of the lizard parents may be

    _____, _____,

    or _____.

12. The likely percentages of gray offspring differ. For the parents in the first Punnett square, the probability of gray offspring will be _____. For the second Punnett square, the probability will be _____.

13. A new genetic allele can be passed to offspring

    A. if a mutation occurs during meiosis.

    B. during fetal development.

    C. after the environment turns a gene off.

    D. during interphase.

Questions 14 and 15 refer to the following diagram.

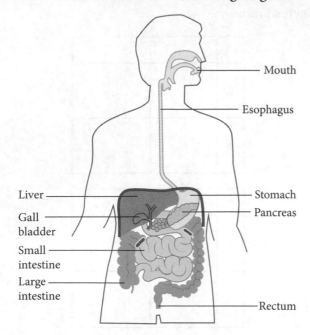

- Mouth
- Esophagus
- Liver
- Gall bladder
- Small intestine
- Large intestine
- Stomach
- Pancreas
- Rectum

14. In general, the small intestine and the large intestine absorb different things from the foods we eat and drink. Food goes from the stomach to the _____, which absorbs nutrients. From there it goes to the _____, which absorbs water.

15. Which of the following is the best example of homeostasis involving your digestive system?

A. salivation in your mouth

B. food traveling down your esophagus

C. a feeling of hunger in your stomach

D. digestion in your small intestine

16. Body systems work together to maintain homeostasis. For example, a receptor in your _____ system senses pain when your finger touches a hot stove. A message goes to the control center, which is your brain. After that, an effector in your _____ system moves your finger away from the stove.

17. Which of the following provides the best evidence to support the hypothesis that black bears are more closely related to panthers than to jellyfish?

A. Black bears and panthers are dark-colored, and jellyfish are translucent.

B. Black bears and panthers live on land, and jellyfish live in water.

C. Black bears and panthers have backbones, and jellyfish do not.

D. Black bears and panthers can form fossils easily, and jellyfish cannot.

18. List four things that support the idea that all living things have common ancestry.

_____

_____

_____

_____

_____

_____

_____

Question 19 refers to the following diagram.

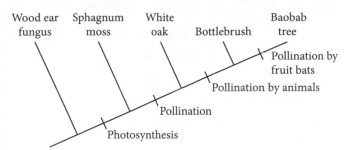

19. According to the cladogram, which species share the trait of using pollination to reproduce?

_____

_____

20. What process has produced such varied canine breeds as Chihuahuas, Great Danes, and poodles from animals whose ancestors were wolves?

_____

21. Which of the following is a selective pressure?

   A. survival of the fittest

   B. natural selection

   C. adaptation

   D. predation

22. Adaptation sometimes results in speciation, but other times it doesn't. What is the defining characteristic of a new species?

_____

Questions 23 and 24 refer to the following diagram.

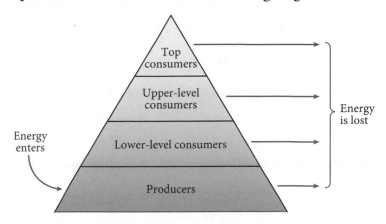

23. Which of these is a correct example of organisms found in an energy pyramid, from top to bottom?

   A. bobcats, foxes, squirrels, insects

   B. foxes, ground squirrels, fungi, trees

   C. mountain lions, foxes, birds, plants with seeds

   D. deer, beavers, snowshoe hares, pine needles

24. Put these organisms in the correct order to form a food chain: foxes, ground squirrels, fungi, trees

   A. _____

   B. _____

   C. _____

   D. _____

25. When a tree falls in the forest, all of these things happen except one. Which of these things is the exception?

   A. Matter from the wood is used by fungi (mushrooms) to grow.

   B. Bacteria begin to decompose the underside of the tree trunk.

   C. More matter is stored in wood during chemical reactions.

   D. Over time, decomposed wood matter becomes soil.

Question 26 refers to the following table.

Common Bacterial Food-borne Illnesses

Bacterium	Found in	Prevention
Campylobacter	Raw or under-cooked poultry	Refrigerate uncooked poultry; cook poultry thoroughly
Salmonella	Meat, eggs, and other animal products	Refrigerate uncooked animal products; cook animal products thoroughly
E. coli	Food contaminated by cow feces	Wash produce; refrigerate foods; cook meat thoroughly

Source: Centers for Disease Control

26. Based on the information in this table, which conclusion would you draw?

   A. Food-borne bacteria get into food when food is brought into a kitchen.

   B. Food-borne bacteria are found only in animal products.

   C. All food should be washed before cooking or eating.

   D. Food-borne bacteria thrive at room temperature.

Questions 27–29 refer to the following scenario.

Many factors can change an ecosystem. Several changes happen at once. Consider a wooded riverside ecosystem. During a heavy storm, much of the area was flooded, plants were blown down, and eggs in nests were broken. Following the storm, the ground and low-growing plants were covered in mud, branches, and leaves. Some of the ponds and streams that provided drinking water were empty because the storm eroded pond edges and riverbanks. Some predators flew or ran away, and some returned when the storm was over.

27. How is the storm likely to affect carrying capacities in the ecosystem?

   A. There will be fewer animals, so competition for limiting resources will decrease.

   B. Some populations will change, which will change the populations of others.

   C. The carrying capacities of swimming species will increase.

   D. Populations of most flying birds will not be affected.

28. In some populations, some members will die in the storm. Other members will fly out to escape the storm. What is another reason some populations may shrink?

   _____

   _____

   _____

   _____

   _____

   _____

29. Which of the following is likely to happen in the ecosystem after the storm?

   A. Alien species will restore balance quickly.

   B. Biodiversity will decrease but may recover.

   C. The normal plant species will overpopulate.

   D. All swimming bird species will be extirpated.

30. What is biodiversity, and how is it affected by extinction?

   _____

   _____

   _____

   _____

   _____

   _____

Unit 2: Physical Science

Lesson 1 — Motion and Forces

Speed

We use words associated with motion and forces every day. You may already have a great understanding of speed! Let's review some definitions.

Distance, Time, and Speed

Distance is the length an object moves from one place to another. Time is the number of seconds or minutes it takes for an object to travel. Speed is the distance traveled in a specific time—that is, distance divided by time.

If you drive a distance of 100 kilometers in 2 hours, your average speed is 100 kilometers ÷ 2 hours = 50 kilometers per hour.

Velocity and Acceleration

Velocity is speed with a direction. If you were driving north in the example, your velocity would be 50 kph north. Acceleration is the rate at which velocity changes. An object accelerates when its speed changes, its direction changes, or both.

A skydiver's initial velocity will be 0 meters per second downward. If she free falls for 10 seconds before opening her parachute, she will fall at a velocity of about 100 meters per second downward. Her change in velocity will be 100 meters per second (100–0). The rate at which her velocity changes will be 100 meters per second divided by 10 seconds. Her acceleration due to the force of **gravity**, then, would be about 10 meters per second per second (per second squared) downward.

> **gravity**—the pull between objects due to their masses

$$\text{Acceleration} = \frac{\text{final velocity–starting velocity}}{\text{time it takes to change velocity}} = \frac{100 \text{ m–0 m}}{10 \text{ s}} = \frac{10 \text{ m}}{\text{s}^2}$$

Mass, Momentum, and Inertia

Mass is the amount of matter in an object. Momentum can be thought of as mass in motion. The momentum of an object is calculated by multiplying its mass by its velocity. A massive object will have more momentum than a less massive object traveling at the same speed. Consider a bowling ball and a golf ball traveling at the same speed down a bowling lane. The bowling ball will have the greater momentum.

Inertia is the tendency for objects to resist a change in motion. If you are in a car that slows down quickly, you will keep moving forward because of inertia. Your seat belt stops this motion. When the car moves forward from a stop, you'll feel the seat's pressure on your back because of your inertia—your tendency to stay still.

The mass of a bowling ball is about 4.5 kg. Suppose the initial forward velocity of a bowling ball is 8 m/s. The momentum of the ball as it leaves the bowler's hand can be calculated like this:

$$\text{Momentum} = \text{mass} \times \text{velocity} = 4.5 \text{ kg} \times 8 \ \frac{\text{meters}}{\text{second}} = 36 \text{ kg} \bullet \text{m/s}$$

Because of inertia, the ball will tend to continue with 36 kg•m/s of momentum toward the pins (we'll ignore friction for now). When the ball hits the pins, its momentum will change because of the collision.

Collisions

system—a set of connected things or parts that form a whole

To study interactions between objects, it is helpful to identify a **system**. In this example, the system includes the ball and pins. (For now, let's ignore the floor and consider only one pin.) Within a system, total momentum does not change. The total momentum after the objects interact will be the same as it was before they interacted. Now we can predict what will happen during a collision.

Total momentum is calculated by adding together the momentum of the objects in a system. So the momentum of the ball plus the momentum of the pin *before* a collision will equal the momentum of the ball plus the momentum of the pin *after* that collision.

The initial momentum of the ball is 36 kg•m/s toward the pin. The momentum of the pin is its mass—about 1.5 kg—times its velocity, which is 0. The pin's momentum is therefore 0. The total momentum of this system before a collision is the momentum of the ball plus the momentum of the pin: 36 kg•m/s.

Next, consider the total momentum after the collision. It is helpful to use mass × velocity in this equation. Subscripts help you keep track of things. The *1* stands for the first object (the ball), and the *2* stands for the second object (the pin). The *i* stands for "initial," and the *f* stands for "final."

$$(mass_1 \times velocity_{1i}) + (mass_2 \times velocity_{2i}) = (mass_1 \times velocity_{1f}) + (mass_2 \times velocity_{2f})$$

There is no *i* or *f* for mass, because mass doesn't change. The only thing that changes is velocity. The ball will tend to keep moving, and it will push the pin. The pin will tend to stay still, so it will push back on the ball and slow it down. If we know the final velocity of one object, we can find the other. Assume the pin will go twice as fast as the initial velocity of the ball and that it will go in the direction the ball was going.

$$(4.5 \text{ kg} \times 8 \text{ m/s}) + (1.5 \text{ kg} \times 0) = (4.5 \text{ kg} \times x \text{ m/s}) + (1.5 \text{ kg} \times 16 \text{ m/s})$$
$$36 \text{ kg•m/s} = (4.5 \text{ kg} \times x \text{ m/s}) + 24 \text{ kg•m/s}$$
$$36 \text{ kg•m/s} - 24 \text{ kg•m/s} = (4.5 \text{ kg} \times x \text{ m/s})$$
$$11 \text{ kg•m/s} \div 4.5 \text{ kg} = x \text{ m/s}$$
$$2.4 \text{ m/s} = x \text{ m/s}$$

The ball's final velocity will be 2.4 m/s, away from the bowler.

Why is it helpful to understand momentum and inertia? Consider this real-world example: When engineers design cars and highway barriers, they assume the barriers will not move if hit by a vehicle. They can determine how momentum and inertia during a collision might affect vehicles and their passengers.

What Is a Force?

A force is simply a push or a pull. You push on a shopping cart to move it forward. You pull on a leash to slow down a dog. In both cases, the force affects the object you apply it to. Pushes and pulls can also be applied without objects touching. Remember, gravitational force (gravity) is a pull between objects due to their masses.

Weight Is a Measure of Force

Weight is a measure of the gravitational force on an object. You are probably used to weight being measured in pounds. In science, force is measured in newtons, named after Sir Isaac Newton. One newton (N) is approximately equal to the weight of a 100-g mass on Earth.

Forces and Motion

In the 1600s, Sir Isaac Newton determined three **laws** that relate forces to motion. Let's explore Newton's second law first. Newton's Second Law of Motion states that the acceleration of an object depends on the mass of the object and the amount of force applied. Force causes an object to accelerate.

> **law**—a summary based on repeated experiments and observations that describes how something in the natural world works

Mathematically, this is expressed as

$$\text{Force} = \text{mass} \times \text{acceleration}$$

Weight and Motion

The weight of an object is its mass multiplied by acceleration due to gravity—about 10 m/s^2, as discussed in the previous section. This acceleration (g) is the increase in velocity as something falls. Weight is a specific example of Newton's Second Law of Motion:

$$\text{Weight} = \text{mass} \times \text{the acceleration due to gravity}$$

Randy weighs 140 pounds, which is 623 N. Given that 1 N = 1 kg•m/s^2, find Randy's mass.

$$\text{Weight (force)} = \text{m (mass)} \times \text{g (acceleration)}$$
$$623 \text{ N} = 623 \text{ kg•m/s}^2 = \text{m} \times 10 \text{ m/s}^2$$
$$62.3 \text{ kg} = \text{m}$$

Randy's mass is 62.3 kg, or 62,300 grams.

Randy and Jake are ice skating. Randy accelerates by 2 m/s^2 and bumps into Jake. Find the magnitude of Randy's push. (Ice skating is a useful example because there is little friction between skates and ice.)

$$F = m \times a$$
$$\text{Force of Randy's push} = \text{Randy's mass} \times \text{Randy's acceleration}$$
$$F = 62.3 \text{ kg} \times 2 \text{ m/s}^2$$
$$F = 124.6 \text{ kg•m/s}^2 = 124.6 \text{ N}$$

Equal and Opposite Force

This brings us to Newton's Third Law of Motion: When one object exerts a force on a second object, the second object exerts an equal and opposite force on the first object. This means that when Randy pushed Jake with 124.6 N of force, Jake pushed Randy back with 124.6 N.

This law helps explain the common movie scene in which one guy punches another guy's face and then shakes his hand in pain: Guy A delivered a force to Guy B's face, but Guy B's face delivered an equal and opposite force to Guy A's hand. Newton's third law also helps explain how you can sit in a chair:

The arrow pointing down indicates the person's weight. The arrow pointing up indicates an equal force that the chair exerts on the person.

Force and Inertia

What if the objects are moving? Here we need Newton's First Law of Motion: An object at rest remains at rest, and an object in motion remains in motion at constant speed and in a straight line unless acted on by an unbalanced force.

The first law brings us back to inertia, the tendency for something that's moving to keep moving and for something that's still to stay still. Newton's first law says that in a system with inertia (as we have on Earth), an object's velocity won't change unless an external force acts on it. That external force can be a push or a pull by another object.

Jake is gliding on the ice. If no one pushes him, he will continue to glide at the same velocity (assuming no friction between his skates and the ice). However, when Randy pushes Jake, Randy exerts an external force. This changes Jake's velocity.

In addition, an equal and opposite force will push Randy, according to Newton's third law. So his velocity will also change. The amount of the change will depend on who has the smaller mass. Objects with less mass need less force applied to get the same effect. If Jake is less massive than Randy, Jake will go faster than Randy after they collide. The increase in speed will also depend on the push—more force has more effect.

The Law of Gravity

Newton's law of gravity is called the *law of universal gravitation*. It can be expressed mathematically:

$$F = G\frac{m_1 m_2}{r^2}$$

F is the force of gravitational attraction between two objects. The m_1 and m_2 stand for the masses of the two objects. The r stands for the distance between the objects, and r^2 is $r \times r$. G is the gravitational constant. Its value is 6.67×10^{-11} N•m²/kg². We can take G out of the equation and still have a helpful law. It would say that the gravitational force between two objects is proportional to what's on the right side of the equation. That is (assuming only one thing on the right changes), as m_1 or m_2 increases, F will increase. As r increases, F will decrease.

What all this means is that any two objects in the universe exert a pull on each other. Small objects exert small pulls that may not be noticeable. Large objects, such as the Earth and the moon, pull enough for us to notice. The larger either mass is (as m_1 or m_2 increases), the more strongly they attract each other. Also, the closer they are to each other, the more strongly they attract each other. As they get farther apart (as r increases), they pull on each other with less force.

We are most familiar with the gravitational attraction between the Earth and everything on its surface (including us). Another example is the attraction within the solar system—gravitational attraction is what keeps the planets in orbit around the sun. The gravitational attraction between the moon and the Earth is what pulls ocean water away from the shore and causes tides.

work—using force to move an object

In ordinary language, work is any effort a person applies to a task. But in science, **work** has a special meaning. In science, work occurs only when a force moves an object it acts on. If there is no movement, there is no work. So if you expend a lot of effort to push a chair but the chair does not move, you haven't done any work! Only when the chair moves does work actually occur.

The amount of work done (W) is equal to the amount of force applied (F) multiplied by the distance (d) the object moves:

$$W = F \times d$$

The unit for work is the newton-meter (N•m), which is called a *joule* (J).

A machine is a device that makes work easier. Machines do not actually reduce the amount of work. Most machines increase the mechanical advantage of the system. That is, they reduce the amount of effort force that is needed to get an object (called a *load*) to move. The trade-off is that they increase the distance over which the effort force must be applied.

Types of Machines

Here are some common types of machines:

Inclined planes—An example of a simple machine that reduces the effort force needed is the inclined plane, or ramp. To move a heavy object straight up requires a lot of force. Pushing the object up a ramp decreases the amount of force needed, but it increases the distance the load must be moved.

Inclined plane

Wedges—Wedges, such as chisels and axes, are also inclined planes.

Screws—A screw is made up of an inclined plane wrapped in a spiral around a shaft.

Levers—Another type of simple machine is the lever. A lever is a rigid bar that pivots at a fixed point, which is called the *fulcrum*. Levers are often used to lift or move heavy loads. With a class one lever, the effort force and load are on opposite sides of the fulcrum, as in a seesaw. With a class two lever, the effort force and load are on the same side of the fulcrum, with the load closer to the fulcrum. Wheelbarrows are class two levers. With a class three lever, the effort force is closer to the fulcrum than the load is. A fishing pole is a class three lever, as is a pair of tweezers.

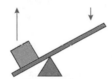
Class one lever

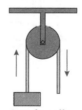
Simple pulley

Pulleys—A pulley is a simple machine with a wheel and rope that can be used to raise or lower objects. A single pulley does not change effort force or the distance the load must travel. It makes work easier by allowing you to pull down on the rope rather than push or pull the load up.

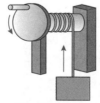
Wheel and axle

Wheel and axle—A wheel and axle is a simple machine that consists of a circular disk that turns around a rod. Wheels help turn, lift, and move objects. A winch is an example. The long winch handle increases the distance over which the effort force is applied while it reduces the effort needed to turn the axle.

Power

power—the amount of work done over a certain period of time. Power is expressed in watts and horsepower

energy—the ability to do work

In addition to making work easier, machines can make work go faster. The rate of doing work—the amount of work done over a specific time—is called **power**. You can calculate power (P) by dividing the amount of work done (W) by the time it took to do the work (t).

$$P = W/t$$

Power is expressed as joules/second, also known as a *watt* (W). You're probably familiar with watts in relation to light bulbs. Bulbs with higher wattage give off more light. Light is not work—it's energy, and **energy** can be defined as the ability to do work. Because of this work-energy relationship, power can be defined as both work done over time, as mentioned above, and energy used over time. Energy used over time is expressed in kilowatt-hours—you can see this unit if you look at your family's electric bill.

Another unit of power is the horsepower (hp). You often hear the term *horsepower* used in relationship with vehicles. Imagine that you are shopping for a truck. Truck A comes with 159 hp, and truck B comes with 411 hp. That means truck B can provide about 2.5 times more power than truck A. What does this mean for you? Power is work over time, so truck B can pull or carry 2.5 times as much weight as truck A can, in the same time. Another way to look at it is that truck B can do the same amount of work in less time, such as ascending a steep hill faster.

Now let's say you are shopping for a car. Car A comes with 100 hp, and car B comes with 1,000 hp. That means car B uses about 10 times more energy than car A over an hour of driving. What does this mean for you? If you're looking to save money on gasoline (or electricity if you have an electric car), you'll want car A.

Guided Practice

Sample Question

Which of the following automotive safety features, if used correctly, is most likely to minimize the risk of whiplash during a rear-end collision?

A. a seatbelt

B. an airbag

C. a headrest

D. safety glass

Think It Through

Hint: Which of the choices would limit head movement?

Q: What is the question asking?

A: Which of the items listed would help prevent whiplash when a car is hit from behind?

Q: What happens during a rear-end collision to cause whiplash?

A: A person's head moves forward with the motion of the car and then snaps backward quickly, due to inertia.

Choice A is incorrect because the seatbelt does not keep the head from moving.

Choice B is incorrect because the airbag is in front of the person.

Choice C is correct because a headrest will stop the head from being jerked back due to inertia.

Choice D is incorrect because safety glass would not affect the head snapping back.

Sample Question

Use Newton's second law to calculate the weight of an orange with a mass of 150 grams. Use metric units. Acceleration due to gravity ≈ 10 m/s^2.

_____

_____

Think It Through

Hint: Weight is an example of Newton's second law.

Q: What is the question asking?

A: It asks you to calculate the weight of an orange.

Q: What is weight?

A: The weight of an object is the amount of gravitational force on it.

Answer:

Force = mass × acceleration is Newton's second law.

Weight = mass × the acceleration due to gravity.

$$= 150 \text{ g} \times 10 \text{ m/s}^2 = 1{,}500 \text{ N}$$

Matter is anything that has mass and takes up space. All matter is made up of particles called *atoms*. Atoms are too small to see, even with a microscope. Atoms themselves are made up of smaller (subatomic) particles called *protons*, *neutrons*, and *electrons*.

Protons are particles with a positive electric charge. Together with neutrons, which have no charge, they make up the nucleus of an atom. The nucleus contains most of the mass in an atom but takes up the least space. Most of the space in an atom is taken up by electrons, which orbit the nucleus. Electrons have a negative electric charge and very little mass. The positive and negative electric charges of the protons and electrons hold an atom together.

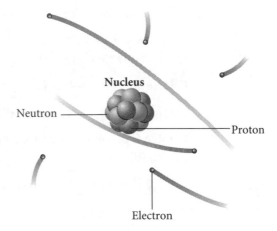

When an atom has an equal number of protons and electrons, it is electrically neutral, or uncharged. When there are more protons, the atom is positively charged. When there are more electrons, the atom is negatively charged. Both types of charged atoms are called *ions*.

Elements   All the atoms of the same type make up one element. Another way to say this is that an element is a substance made up of only one type of atom. An element you are familiar with is gold. In theory, a 24-carat (pure) gold ring contains only gold atoms. What makes them gold atoms? Each one has 79 protons. The number of protons in an atom is the element's atomic number. Elements are often represented by chemical symbols—one- or two-letter abbreviations—such as these: C for carbon, H for hydrogen, O for oxygen, N for nitrogen, Na for sodium, and Cl for chlorine.

Physical and Chemical Properties

isotopes—atoms of the same element that have different masses

Although the atoms of an element all have the same number of protons, the number of neutrons can vary. These variations result in **isotopes**. For example, the element carbon has 6 protons. Almost 99% of carbon atoms have 6 protons and 6 neutrons. However, 1% of carbon atoms have 7 neutrons. A very few carbon atoms have 8 neutrons. That means that there are at least three isotopes of carbon. The extra neutrons add to the mass of the isotope. They don't alter its charge, though, since neutrons have no charge.

Compounds

All substances are made up of atoms. But atoms don't usually exist by themselves. Instead, they combine with other atoms. The unique combination of electric charges in each element gives it something like a personality. That is, the charges make some elements more attractive to certain others. Because of these attractions, atoms bond together in compounds.

A compound is a substance made up of atoms of two or more elements always combined in the same ratio. For example, water is a compound made up of hydrogen (H) and oxygen (O) in a ratio of 2 to 1. The composition of a compound can be represented by its chemical formula. In the case of water, that's H_2O. The subscript ($_2$) means there are two hydrogen atoms. The lack of a subscript means there is only one oxygen atom.

Chemical Bonds

molecule—a group of atoms held together by a covalent bond

There are two main types of compounds. They are the results of the two main types of chemical bonds: covalent bonds and ionic bonds. In a covalent bond, two atoms share a pair of electrons. A covalently bonded compound is called a **molecule**. There are molecules of all kinds and sizes. For example, some protein molecules contain thousands of bonded atoms. Other molecules, such as carbon monoxide, contain only two atoms. (A few elements occur naturally as molecules even though they are not compounds. For example, oxygen in the air is a molecule containing two oxygen atoms: O_2.)

In an ionic bond, one atom loses an electron to the other. This makes one positive ion and one negative ion, which attract each other. The attraction makes an ionic compound, which is not technically a molecule. In spite of their weaker bonds, ionic compounds are very common. Table salt—sodium chloride (NaCl)—is one. The left side of the diagram below shows how covalent bonds hold together a water molecule. The right side shows how ionic bonds hold sodium chloride together.

2 hydrogen atoms and 1 oxygen atom

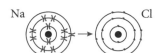

1 sodium atom and 1 chlorine atom

H_2O

Covalent Bond

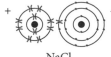

NaCl

Ionic Bond

Physical and Chemical Properties

Physical and Chemical Properties

All matter has physical and chemical properties. Physical properties are characteristics that can be observed. Physical properties such as mass and volume depend on the amount of matter being observed. Other physical properties include color, hardness, the ability to conduct electricity and heat, and odor. Another is elasticity—the ability of a substance to go back to its original shape and size after it's stretched. Another, tensile strength, is a measure of how much a substance can be stretched before it breaks. Density is a physical property that combines two others—mass and volume.

States of Matter

Another important physical property is state: the physical form in which a substance exists. Matter usually occurs in one of three physical states: solid, liquid, or gas. (There is also an uncommon fourth state called *plasma*.) A solid has a definite shape and volume. A liquid has a definite volume but takes the shape of part of its container. A gas has neither a definite volume nor a definite shape, so a gas occupies the entire container it's in.

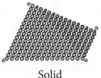

Solid   Liquid   Gas

According to the kinetic theory of matter, the properties of solids, liquids, and gases are due to the behavior of the particles that make them up, as shown in the diagram. In a solid, the particles are tightly packed and have fixed positions. In a liquid, the particles are close but still move around. In a gas, the particles are far from each other between collisions and move at high speed.

Changes of State

Matter can undergo a physical change from one state to another when energy is added or removed from the system. These changes of state take place at different temperatures for different substances. For example, liquid water freezes at 0°C and boils at 100°C. Mercury, on the other hand, freezes at –39°C and boils at 357°C. Changes of state are summarized in the chart below.

State Change	Processes	Examples
Solid to liquid	Melting, liquefying	Melting of snow or ice
Solid to gas	Sublimation	Sublimation of dry ice (frozen carbon dioxide)
Liquid to solid	Freezing, solidifying	Freezing of water into ice
Liquid to gas	Boiling, vaporization, evaporation	Evaporation of water into water vapor
Gas to liquid	Condensation, liquefying	Formation of dew
Gas to solid	Condensation, deposition	Formation of frost

Balancing Chemical Equations

Chemical Properties

Unlike physical properties, the chemical properties of matter can only be observed during chemical reactions. Chemical properties of substances include the types of chemical bonds they will form, how much they will react with other substances, whether they are chemically stable, whether they are combustible (will burn), and how much heat they will give off when burned. These and other chemical properties can be used to predict what substances will do during reactions.

Mixtures

> **classification of matter**—all matter can be classified as atoms, elements, compounds, or mixtures.

Before we go on to chemical reactions, we should consider mixtures. A mixture is a reversible combination of two or more substances. Those substances keep their individual chemical properties and can be separated again to show their individual physical properties. The substances in a mixture can occur in any proportion, and one part of a mixture may differ from another part. Most foods are mixtures. For example, milk is a mixture of water, proteins, carbohydrates, fats, vitamins, and minerals. Other examples of mixtures include soil and air.

Mixtures can be separated into their parts in several ways. Sometimes a mixture separates on its own. For example, a mixture of oil and vinegar will separate into two layers if it is not shaken or stirred for a while. A mixture of carbon dioxide gas and water, found in soft drinks, will separate when the gas escapes into the air. A mixture of salt and water will separate when the water evaporates, leaving the salt behind.

Balancing Chemical Equations

> **product**—a substance formed as the result of a chemical reaction

Unlike mixtures, the substances that undergo chemical reactions do not keep their individual properties. There are some chemical reactions that are reversible. In many, though, the **products** cannot be changed back into the original substances.

One way to represent what happens in a chemical reaction is to use a chemical equation. The burning of methane can be shown like this:

$$CH_4 + 2O_2 \rightarrow CO_2 + 2H_2O$$

This means that one molecule of methane (CH_4) and two molecules of oxygen ($2O_2$) react to form one molecule of carbon dioxide (CO_2) and two molecules of water ($2H_2O$). Notice that the number of atoms of each element on the left of the arrow is the same as the number of atoms of each element on the right. This is always true in a balanced chemical equation. In the equation, there are 4 hydrogen atoms, 1 carbon atom, and 4 oxygen atoms on each side. (Multiply the coefficient 2 by the subscript 2 to get the number of oxygen atoms in $2O_2$.) To balance a chemical equation, you may change the number of molecules of an element or compound, but you may not change any compound formulas.

Law of Conservation of Mass

> **law of conservation of mass**—scientific law that states that mass is neither created nor destroyed during chemical and physical reactions

A balanced chemical equation illustrates the **law of conservation of mass:** matter can neither be created nor destroyed. It simply changes form. If you measure the total mass of the reactants (substances before the reaction) and the total mass of the products (substances after the reaction), they will be equal.

What is an *un*balanced chemical equation? Here is an example.

$$CO_2 + H_2O \rightarrow C_6H_{12}O_6 + O_2$$

This is the basic equation used in the discussion of photosynthesis. It means that carbon dioxide and water react to form glucose (a sugar) and molecular oxygen.

Notice that there are no coefficients in the equation. Coefficients are the numbers before the formulas, such as the "2" in $2O_2$. Also notice that the number of carbon atoms on the left of the arrow does not equal the number of carbon atoms on the right. The same is true of the oxygen atoms and the hydrogen atoms. This brings us to the concept of limiting reactants.

Limiting Reactants

A chemical reaction is limited by the amounts and ratio of substances that are available to react. For example, in the photosynthesis reaction, if there is plenty of carbon dioxide but not enough water, there will be no photosynthesis. (This is one reason why we need to water our plants.) How much water is needed? We can find out by balancing the chemical equation and then measuring in moles. In general, chemical amounts can be given in moles. A **mole** of some substance is about 6.02×10^{23} molecules of it (that's Avogadro's number, which is close to 6 trillion trillion). How many moles of water do we need for our plants?

> **mole**—a unit of measurement used to express amounts of a chemical substance

First, balance the equation. Start by adding a coefficient to some reactant. Then count up the numbers of atoms, and compare them to the numbers of atoms in the products. For example, adding a coefficient of 2 to CO_2 will give us 2 carbon atoms, but there are 6 carbon atoms in the products. They don't match, so we try again with a coefficient of 6 in front of the CO_2. That makes the carbon atoms match on both sides of the equation. Do the other numbers of atoms match, too?

$$6CO_2 + H_2O \rightarrow C_6H_{12}O_6 + O_2$$

No, now there are 13 oxygen atoms on the left but 8 on the right. We can balance this equation by changing the coefficients and then comparing the numbers of atoms. Here is the balanced equation:

$$6CO_2 + 6H_2O \rightarrow C_6H_{12}O_6 + 6O_2$$

Now, there are 6 C atoms, 18 O atoms, and 12 H atoms on each side of the arrow. From the balanced equation, we can see how many moles of water we need for every mole of carbon dioxide. The number of moles is the same as the coefficient. This is true because the ratio is the same whether we consider molecules or moles. The ratio is 1 mole CO_2 to 1 mole H_2O. However, there must be 6 moles of each to make 1 mole of glucose ($C_6H_{12}O_6$). If there are fewer than 6 moles of water, even though there is an unlimited amount of carbon dioxide (from the air), the plant cannot make glucose. So in this chemical reaction, water is the limiting reactant.

Types of Reactions

There are different kinds of chemical reactions. Here are a few:

Combustion reaction A combustible reactant combines with something like oxygen, and heat is generated as the products are made. This is what happens in the burning of methane, as mentioned on page 51: $CH_4 + 2O_2 \rightarrow CO_2 + 2H_2O$.

Combination reaction Two or more reactants make a more complex product: $A + B \rightarrow AB$. ("A" and "B" here are stand-ins for other element symbols.)

Decomposition reaction A complex reactant is broken down into smaller products: $AB \rightarrow A + B$.

Single-displacement reaction One element is removed from a compound and another takes its place: A + BC → AC + B.

Acid-base reaction Two elements are displaced, and the reactants are an acid and a base: HA + BOH → H_2O + BA.

Solutions

Some substances can be made without chemical reactions—solutions, for example. A solution is the result of mixing. It is a special type of mixture. In a solution, the mixture of substances is the same throughout. Every part of a solution is the same as every other part—same ratio of substances, same density, and same appearance. A solution is made up of a solvent and one or more solutes that are dissolved in it. For example, simple sugar syrup is a solution. It consists of water (the solvent) and sugar (the solute) that is dissolved in the water.

In a solution, the particles of solute are very small—the size of molecules. Solvents as well as solutes can be solid, liquid, or gas. For example, seltzer water is a solution of carbon dioxide gas dissolved in liquid water. Steel is a solution of carbon dissolved in iron. Vinegar is a solution of liquid acetic acid dissolved in water. Different solutions have different strengths. Food-grade vinegar is a weak solution. More acetic acid could be dissolved in water to make a strong solution. But that solution would be found in a chemistry lab, not in a grocery store.

saturation—the point at which no more solute will dissolve in a solution

To prepare a solution of salt and water, you would add salt to the water and stir. Eventually, as you added more salt, you would reach a point where no more salt would dissolve. Instead, salt would begin to settle to the bottom of the container. When this happens—when no more solute will dissolve in a solution—the solution is referred to as saturated. It has reached the point of **saturation**.

Solubility

The amount of a substance that will dissolve in a solvent is known as the solubility of that substance. Some substances are more soluble than others. Also, many substances are more soluble in one solvent than in another. For example, not much olive oil will dissolve in vinegar (or vice versa). That's why many salad dressings separate while they sit on the shelf. Another solubility factor is temperature. For example, at room temperature (20°C), 35.7 grams of table salt can dissolve in 100 milliliters of water. But salt's solubility increases to 39.7 grams per 100 milliliters of water if the water is boiling (100°C).

Temperature isn't the only factor that affects how much solute will dissolve. When heating is impossible or difficult, mixing will help. An everyday example of this is the two different ways to make sweetened tea. One way is to add the sugar while the tea is hot. After the sugar dissolves, you let the tea cool down. Another way is to add sugar to tea that is already cool. In that case, you can get much more sugar to dissolve if you stir it.

Solutions are mixtures, so the substances in them can be separated. The typical way to separate a solution is by distillation. In distillation, the solvent is boiled away, condensed, and collected, and the solute remains behind. This is how distilled water is made from tap water. Distillation is also the process used to purify seawater to make it drinkable.

Guided Practice

Sample Question Which of these are products of the chemical reaction shown?

$$4H_2 + 2O_2 \rightarrow 4H_2O$$

A. 4 water molecules

B. 8 hydrogen atoms

C. 2 oxygen molecules

D. 4 hydrogen molecules

Think It Through

Hint: What is H_2O?

Q: What is the question asking?

A: The question asks which choice represents products of the chemical reaction.

Q: What are products?

A: Products are the substances formed as a result of a chemical reaction. So the products are to the right of the arrow.

Choice A is correct. There are 4 water molecules on the right side of the arrow.

Choices B, C, and D are incorrect because they are on the left of the arrow.

Sample Question In a replacement reaction, one element is replaced by another in a compound. For example, in this reaction, iron replaces the hydrogen that was bonded to the sulfate:

$$Fe + H_2SO_4 \rightarrow FeSO_4 + H_2$$

In the chemical equation shown, which of these is a reactant?

A. H_2O

B. Fe

C. $FeSO_4$

D. H_2

Think It Through

Hint: The arrow in a chemical equation tells you the direction of the reaction.

Q: What is the question asking?

A: Which chemical is a reactant?

Q: What is a reactant?

A: The reactants are the substances before the reaction takes place. In this equation, the reactants are to the left of the arrow.

Choice A is incorrect because it is not in the equation.

Choice B is correct.

Choices C and D are incorrect because they are part of the product or the result of the reaction.

We use the word *heat* in a number of ways in regular conversation. In science, though, heat has a more limited definition. Another important definition is the one for *temperature*. Both definitions rely on an understanding of the term *thermal energy*. Let's start with energy in general.

Energy is not a simple concept, though we all have some understanding of it. In an earlier section, energy was defined as the ability to do work. Energy can also be defined as a characteristic of matter seen in the movements of particles in a substance. Where there is light, heat, sound, or movement, there is energy. Kinetic energy is the energy of motion.

Thermal energy is the total kinetic energy of all particles in a substance. You can think of this as the total random motion of the particles. If it seems odd that thermal energy is related to motion, consider how water bubbles when it boils.

Temperature is a measure of the average—not the total—kinetic energy of the particles in a substance. For example, a small pot of boiling water and a large pot of boiling water will have the same temperature (average kinetic energy). However, the thermal energy (total kinetic energy) of the water in the large pot will be greater because there is more water, and therefore more particles.

Heat is the energy transferred from one object to another object that has a lower temperature. Heat is not the same as thermal energy.

> **thermal energy**—the total kinetic energy of all particles in a substance. Thermal energy is not the same thing as *heat*.

Heat Transfer

How does heat—the energy that is transferred—move from one thing to another? In solids, heat moves by conduction. In liquids and gases, heat moves by convection. In empty space, heat moves by radiation.

Conduction is the transfer of energy from one particle to the next while the particles stay in one place. In the illustration below, the bottom of the pan warms up first. Heat travels from particles of higher temperature to particles of lower temperature. The heat spreads from one metal particle to the next, finally reaching the handle. If the handle is made of a different material (most are not metal), the heat will not move as quickly through it. That's because conduction of heat is a physical property that differs for different materials.

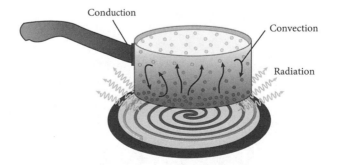

Conduction

Convection

Radiation

Convection is the transfer of energy from one particle to the next while the particles move around and over each other. In the illustration, the arrows in the pot indicate that the particles move in many directions. As with conduction, the end result is that heat moves from warmer to cooler particles.

Convection happens in air as well as in liquids. As air gains energy, its particles move farther apart (it gets less dense). The cooler (more dense) air then sinks below the warmer air. This creates a convection current as the cold air is warmed and the warmer air cools, and the cool air then sinks again.

Radiation is the transfer of energy in waves (more about these later). Unlike conduction and convection, radiation does not require that particles touch each other. For that reason, radiation can travel through space, and it easily travels though air, as shown in the illustration.

Work and Conservation of Energy

People use the properties of energy and the transfer of heat to keep warm, of course, but also to do work. For example, in a typical car engine, the energy stored in gasoline is combusted (burned) to make pistons move, which turns the drive wheels and moves people and things from one place to another. Not all the energy is captured to do work, though. Some energy is used to warm the air in the passenger compartment. A bit more is captured and used to generate electric power. The rest is lost as waste heat.

law of conservation of energy—the law that states that energy is neither created nor destroyed

The **law of conservation of energy** states that energy is neither created nor destroyed. But energy can change from one form to another, and it can enter or leave a system. If you think of a car filled with gasoline as a system, then the waste heat leaves that system. It usually moves into the air, which is part of the environment—a larger system. If the car is in Nome, Alaska, and you live there, you might be happy to have that extra heat. In most places, though, the energy really is wasted, even in the larger system. A more efficient car needs less energy. And it will need less energy if it loses less waste heat to the environment.

Exothermic and Endothermic Reactions

We know that energy cannot be created or destroyed, but it can enter or leave a system. How does this apply to exothermic and endothermic chemical reactions?

Energy Is Released

Here is the equation for methane combustion:

$$CH_4 + 2O_2 \rightarrow CO_2 + 2H_2O$$

Burning methane is much like burning gasoline—the energy stored in methane is transformed to heat and some light. The change in energy isn't shown in a balanced chemical equation. However, in any chemical reaction, energy is transferred from some atoms to others, and the amount of energy stored in the system of reactants and products does change.

Methane (CH_4) stores a lot of energy (there's a lot of motion in its particles). When it reacts with O_2, the products CO_2 and H_2O are not high-energy molecules. Where does the energy go? As with a car's waste heat, the energy leaves this system of reactants and products. (Most of the heat is recovered to do things like warm buildings and generate electricity.) A chemical reaction that releases energy is called *exothermic* (*exo*-means "out," and *thermo* refers to heat). Combustion reactions are exothermic chemical reactions.

As the graph shows, there is also an input of energy to the system that gets the reaction started. This is called **activation energy.** In an exothermic reaction, the activation energy going into the system is less than the total amount of energy coming out.

activation energy—the minimum amount of energy needed for substances to react

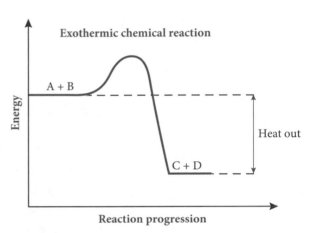

Energy Is Stored

Here is the balanced equation for photosynthesis:

$$6CO_2 + 6H_2O \rightarrow C_6H_{12}O_6 + 6O_2$$

In this reaction, carbon dioxide and water (CO_2 and H_2O) are not high-energy molecules. When they react, the input of energy is stored in glucose ($C_6H_{12}O_6$). In this reaction, the activation energy going into the system is more than the total amount of energy coming out of the system. A chemical reaction that stores energy from the environment is called *endothermic* (*endo*- means "in" and *thermo* refers to heat). This photosynthesis reaction is an endothermic chemical reaction.

Energy has not been created or destroyed in either of these reactions, but it has entered or left the system. It has come from, or gone to, the environment. What is the environment? For methane combustion, consider a chemistry laboratory to be a larger system that holds the reaction system. In this larger system, no energy enters or leaves—it just changes form. Some of the energy that was stored in the fast-moving particles of methane moves out into the air of the lab. It is noticeable as light (in a flame) and as an increase in air temperature.

For the photosynthesis reaction, the larger system includes the reactants, the organism undergoing photosynthesis, the air (where CO_2 comes from), the soil (where H_2O comes from), and the sun. In this case, the environment is what we typically think of as the environment.

Theoretically, there are only three types of energy: potential energy, kinetic energy, and energy in fields.

The potential energy of a molecule (such as CH_4) can be thought of as the energy it stores. The potential energy of a large object can be thought of as the energy it has because of its position or condition. The diagram below shows a pendulum. As the ball swings back and forth, its potential energy changes. At the bottom of the swing, in the center, it has the least potential energy. At the top of the swing, on either side, it has the most potential energy. The higher it swings, the more potential energy it has. Also, the larger its mass is, the more potential energy it has. The total energy—kinetic plus potential—is the object's **mechanical energy**.

> **mechanical energy—** the sum of potential energy and kinetic energy. The mechanical energy of an object represents both its energy of movement and its energy of position.

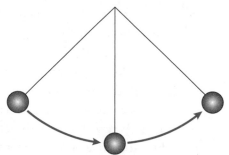

What causes the pendulum to swing up in the first place? Energy has to be added to the system to get the ball going. However, after that, kinetic energy takes over. Kinetic energy can be thought of as random movement of particles. The kinetic energy of a large object like a pendulum can be thought of as the energy it has because of its motion. It's related to momentum, discussed on pages 41 and 42.

As potential energy decreases, kinetic energy increases, and vice versa. So at the top of the swing, the system has the most potential energy and no kinetic energy (when the ball has no motion). As the ball swings down, it loses potential energy, but it speeds up. At its greatest speed, at the bottom of the swing, it has the most kinetic energy. At that point, it has zero potential energy. In fact, the amount of potential energy at the top of the swing equals the amount of kinetic energy at the bottom of the swing.

Subtypes of Energy

In addition to potential and kinetic energy, there is the energy in fields. This includes the energy between charged particles, between magnets, and in electromagnetic radiation (such as light). Energy of these three types—potential, kinetic, and field energy—shows itself as light, heat, and sound, and other subtypes. It can also be detected when there is motion, magnetism, or electricity. People use a number of other terms to describe subtypes of energy. These terms are listed in the table.

Common Term	Energy Type
energy of motion	kinetic energy
stored energy	potential energy
chemical energy	potential energy stored in chemical compounds
electrical energy	potential energy stored in batteries or electric field energy (delivered in current)
light energy	electromagnetic field energy in the visible spectrum
sound energy	kinetic energy traveling in waves

Energy Transformations

Any type of energy can be changed into another type of energy. For example, let's follow the energy transformations that occur in and around this archer.

1. The sun's energy in an electromagnetic field is captured by leaves and transformed, through photosynthesis, into potential energy in the molecules of an oak tree.

2. Potential energy in acorns is transformed into kinetic and potential energy in a squirrel when it eats the acorns. The squirrel uses some kinetic energy to move around and stay warm. Some potential energy is stored in the squirrel's molecules.

3. The archer uses kinetic energy to draw back the string of the bow. This transforms the archer's kinetic energy into the potential energy of the bow. The bow's potential energy is due to its condition (stretched). This is generally called *elastic potential energy*. Like a rubber band, the bow is elastic—it can be stretched and will return to its original shape when force is no longer applied.

4. When the archer lets the arrow go, the bow's potential energy is transformed into kinetic energy of the bow as the string moves forward. This energy is transferred to the arrow. The arrow's kinetic energy keeps it in motion until it hits the target.

We use energy for work, for play (such as watching TV), and to help us with necessary life functions (such as cooking). We get some of this energy from fossil fuels, where it has been stored for millions of years. The fossil fuels that we buy and use directly include gasoline, propane, and natural gas. Electric power generation also makes use of fossil fuels. In fact, in the United States in 2013, 39 percent of our electric power was generated through coal combustion. Another 27 percent came from natural gas combustion, and 1 percent came from combustion of oil.

There are other energy sources that are used for power generation. Nuclear fission powered 20 percent of U.S. electricity production in 2010. About 11 percent came from renewable energy sources—hydropower, wind power, geothermal energy, and solar power. About 1.4 percent of the renewable sources was biomass, such as farm crop waste, suburban yard waste, and manure.

Cost of Energy Sources

Sources of energy differ in many ways, including cost, availability, and environmental effects. The relative cost of generating electricity, from most expensive to least expensive, is shown in this table:

Energy Source	Relative Cost
Solar energy	highest
Hydrogen for fuel cells	
Wind (offshore)	
Biomass	
Uranium for nuclear fission	
Coal	
Landfill gas	
Hydropower	
Wind (on land)	
Geothermal energy	
Natural gas	lowest

Capacity for Producing Energy

Unfortunately, we can't always produce electric power in the least expensive way. As the next table shows, we don't have a large capacity for some of the least expensive energy sources. That means two things. First, we may not have a large number of the specific machines and equipment needed to use a particular energy source. Second, that energy source may not be easy to obtain. Both of these things are true in the case of **geothermal energy**. We don't have many geothermal energy power plants, and there are few places in the United States where we can tap into geothermal energy.

geothermal energy— thermal energy generated and stored in the Earth

Energy Source	U.S. Capacity
Uranium for nuclear fission	highest
Coal	
Hydropower	
Natural gas	
Solar energy	
Wind (offshore)	
Biomass	
Wind (on land)	
Geothermal	
Landfill gas	
Hydrogen for fuel cells	lowest

Environmental Effects

Another factor that should be considered when an energy source is used is how it affects the environment. One of the most obvious effects of electric power generation is air pollution. Air pollutants include carbon dioxide, sulfur dioxide, nitrogen oxides, particulates, and mercury. The next table compares the emissions of those air pollutants from various energy sources, from most polluting to least polluting:

Energy Source	Air Pollution
Coal	high
Natural gas	medium
Biomass	low
Geothermal	low
Landfill gas	low
Hydropower	none
Uranium for nuclear fission	none
Solar energy	none
Wind offshore	none
Wind on land	none
Hydrogen for fuel cells	none

Today and in the recent past, fossil fuels have been the most used energy sources, especially for transportation. The mix has changed over time and will continue to change as costs and capacity change. New awareness of the effects of carbon dioxide has shifted energy use for cars. For example, more electric-powered vehicles are being made. When the electric power is produced from clean energy sources, this can make a big difference in air pollution.

With present-day technology, solar power is expensive, and we don't have the capacity to use much of it yet. However, the U.S. solar industry is growing rapidly. Where it is already being used, it produces no air pollution. It is available daily and is in unlimited supply.

A wave is a disturbance that repeats itself, usually in a pattern. A wave moves energy from one place to another without moving matter with it. That is, particles or large amounts of matter may be moved, but not in the direction that the energy is moved. Any matter that is moved returns to its original place after the wave has gone. Ocean waves, seismic waves in the Earth's crust, and sound waves are examples of waves. There are two main types of waves—longitudinal waves and transverse waves.

Longitudinal Waves

In a longitudinal wave, the disturbance is parallel to the direction of the energy flow. In the diagram, you can see that the particles (what look like loops of a spring) move back and forth along the same line as the energy. In the compressions, the particles move closer together. In the rarefactions, they move apart. Longitudinal waves can travel through matter but not through space. Sound waves are examples of longitudinal waves. They usually travel through air to reach our ears. They can also travel through liquids and solids.

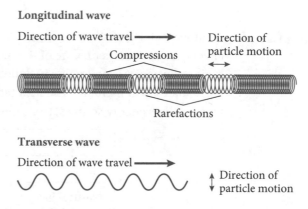

Longitudinal wave

Direction of wave travel ⟶   Direction of particle motion ⟷

Compressions

Rarefactions

Transverse wave

Direction of wave travel ⟶   Direction of particle motion ↕

Transverse Waves

In a transverse wave, the direction of the disturbance is perpendicular to the energy flow. Notice in the diagram of the transverse wave that the particles move up and down while the energy travels from left to the right. Water waves, like those that result from dropping a pebble in a pond, are transverse waves.

Waves of all types have some common characteristics. They are easy to see in a diagram of a transverse wave like the one above. **Wavelength** is the distance between two crests (highest points) of a wave. Frequency is the number of crests that pass a point over time. Frequency and wavelength are connected to wave speed. Amplitude is crest height and increases as the energy of the wave increases.

wavelength—the distance between one point on a wave and the corresponding point on the next wave

Electromagnetic waves, including light waves, are transverse waves. Instead of being disturbances in matter as water waves are, electromagnetic waves are disturbances in electric and magnetic fields. Because they don't use matter to move energy, electromagnetic waves can travel through the emptiness of space. The sun's energy reaches us in the form of electromagnetic waves.

Waves

The Electromagnetic Spectrum

There is a spectrum (a range of varieties) of electromagnetic waves. They vary in wavelength and frequency. At one end of the spectrum are radio waves, with wavelengths several miles long and low frequencies. Radio waves are used for radio, television, and radar. Short radio waves are the familiar microwaves that we use for cooking. In the middle of the spectrum, infrared radiation carries heat. These waves are used in warming lamps and can be detected by night-vision goggles. Visible light carries energy that we can see. Ultraviolet radiation, often called UV light, can sterilize medical equipment but also can damage our skin. X-rays are used to take images of dense matter such as teeth. Gamma rays, with the shortest wavelengths, are very dangerous but are used in some forms of radiation treatments for cancer.

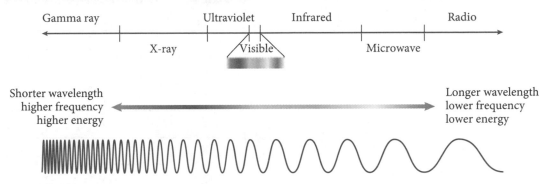

The energy of large ranges of wavelengths can be used together, in computers and other electronic information equipment. For example, light and infrared waves, microwaves, and radio waves are used to make digital signals that can be picked up by cell phones and wireless networks. The different waves are used to make different patterns to code information. The codes can then be saved, sent, and copied, as computer users do all the time.

Notice from the diagram of the electromagnetic spectrum that gamma rays have short wavelengths and high frequency. On the opposite end of the diagram, radio waves have long waves and low frequencies. Wave speed equals wavelength times frequency, so as the wavelength increases, the frequency decreases, and vice versa. This is tied to the fact that all electromagnetic waves have the same speed in space—what we call the speed of light (about 300 million meters per second). You may have heard this called the speed of light in a **vacuum**. This is because space has no (or very few) particles in it. In Earth's atmosphere, the speed of light is slower than in space.

vacuum—the absence of matter

Sample Question   Students conducted an experiment to test their hypothesis that solar panels work better on warmer days. They connected a photovoltaic cell (a solar collector) to a voltmeter (which measures electricity). At noon on every school day in the month of May, they checked whether there was full sun outside. If there was, they put the photovoltaic cell and voltmeter outside in direct sun, along with a thermometer. Once the thermometer reading stopped changing, they recorded the temperature and the voltmeter reading. Here were their results:

Date in May	Temperature (°F)	Electricity Generation (volts)
1	70	4.0
2	61	4.5
7	65	4.3
8	90	3.9
14	67	3.6
16	66	4.1
19	73	3.9
20	77	4.5
26	78	3.5
28	86	4.2

What would be the most precise way to state the students' hypothesis?

A. Solar panels work better on warmer days.

B. Photovoltaic panels produce more electricity in brighter sun.

C. Photovoltaic panel voltage depends on temperature.

D. Solar panel voltage increases as temperature increases.

Think It Through   **Q:** What is the question asking?

A: It asks which option most precisely states the hypothesis for the students' experiment.

Q: Which option uses precise or exact wording?

A: Read the choices, and look for a precise, correct statement.

Hint: Some incorrect answer options are true statements. Read the question carefully to make sure you choose the best answer.

Choices A, B, and C are incorrect because "work better" and "produce more" are vague, and "depends on" doesn't clearly describe the relationship.

Choice D is correct because it clearly states the relationship between solar panel voltage and temperature.

Guided Practice

Sample Question

Which of the following statements is correct about the experiment?

A. The students' hypothesis is supported by the data.

B. The data show that temperature depends on voltage.

C. Voltage was the dependent variable.

D. Temperature was the dependent variable.

Think It Through

Q: What is the question asking?

A: Which choice is a correct statement about the experiment?

Q: Which statement is supported by the data in the table?

A: Read across the rows of the table to see the data students recorded.

Choices A and B are incorrect. The data in the table do not show any correlation between temperature and electricity generation.

Choice C is correct. Voltage was the dependent variable. The dependent variable is the outcome of the experiment or the thing you are studying. So, Choice D is incorrect.

Sample Question

Which is an example of electromagnetic radiation?

A. ripples on a lake

B. music from a trumpet

C. ultraviolet light from the sun

D. seismic waves from an earthquake

Think It Through

Q: What is the question asking?

A: It asks which option is an example of electromagnetic radiation.

Q: What do you know about electromagnetic radiation?

Hint: Remember that electromagnetic waves travel at the speed of light.

A: Radio waves and light waves are on the spectrum of electromagnetic radiation.

Choices A and D are incorrect because the waves cause disturbances in matter.

Choice B is incorrect because sound waves are longitudinal waves.

Choice C is correct because light of any type is electromagnetic radiation.

Guided Practice

Sample Question A group of students tested the effect of moving the fulcrum of a class one lever away from the load. They measured the amount of effort force required to lift the load until the lever was level. The graph shows their results.

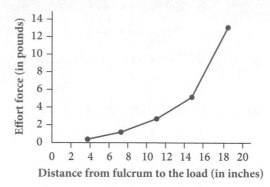

Which generalization about class one levers is supported by the data on this graph?

A. As distance from the fulcrum to the load decreases, effort force increases.

B. As distance from the fulcrum to the load increases, effort force increases.

C. As the load increases, effort force decreases.

D. As the load increases, effort force increases.

Think It Through Q: What is the question asking?

A: Which choice is supported by the graph?

Hint: Read the graph. What trend does the line graph show?

Q: What happens as the distance from the fulcrum to the load increases?

A: The graph shows that the effort force also increases.

Choice A is incorrect because it contradicts the graph.

Choice B is correct. As distance from the fulcrum to the load increases, effort force increases.

Choices C and D are incorrect because the graph gives no information about increasing the load.

Sample Question Sophie used a shovel to pry a large rock out of the ground. When used this way, a shovel is a _____, a type of simple machine.

Think It Through Q: What is the question asking?

A: It asks what type of machine a shovel is when it is used to pry a rock out of the ground.

Hint: Which type of machine works like a seesaw to lift heavy objects?

Q: What are some types of simple machines?

A: Inclined planes, wedges, screws, levers, pulleys, wheels, and axles.

Answer: lever

Questions 1 and 2 refer to the graph below.

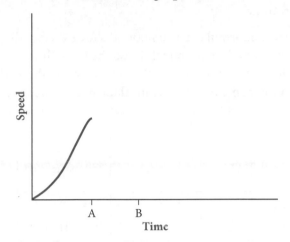

1. A cyclist accelerates to high speed and then takes her feet off the pedals. Her change in speed until time A is shown on the graph. Which of these is a good hypothesis about what will happen between time A and time B?

    A. Her forward acceleration will increase.

    B. Her forward momentum will decrease.

    C. More mass will lead to more speed.

    D. Less mass will lead to less speed.

2. What is the dependent variable in this observation?

    A. time

    B. mass

    C. speed

    D. momentum

3. Which of the following statements is true?

    A. Light is a type of thermal energy.

    B. Kinetic energy is a type of electrical energy.

    C. Chemical energy is a type of potential energy.

    D. Kinetic energy is the same as mechanical energy.

Question 4 refers to the following information and diagram.

When a force is applied to an object, the result depends not only on that force but also on all the other forces acting on that object. An object that is not moving often has a number of forces acting on it, but the sum of those forces is zero. If the total force on an object is not zero, however, its motion will change.

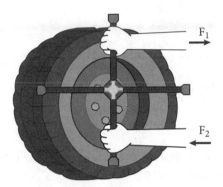

4. What is the result of the application of forces (F_1 and F_2) on the lug wrench?

    A. The lug wrench turns the lug nut clockwise.

    B. The lug wrench turns the lug nut counterclockwise.

    C. The lug wrench presses the lug nut straight down.

    D. Nothing happens because the forces are equal.

5. Which of these is NEVER the result of a force?

    A. change in mass

    B. change in direction

    C. decreased velocity

    D. increased momentum

Question 6 refers to the following information and diagram.

In a simple machine such as a pulley or an inclined plane, work is input by the application of a force to the machine. Energy is lost as the machine performs, as indicated by this diagram.

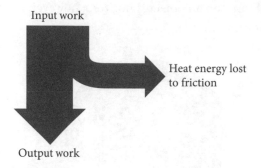

Input work

Heat energy lost to friction

Output work

6. Which generalization is supported by the information and diagram?

A. The amount of output work a machine performs is always less than the amount of input work.

B. The more efficient the machine, the more heat energy it loses due to friction.

C. Simple machines are less efficient than machines that are powered by electricity.

D. A machine can keep working forever, even when work input is stopped.

7. Explain the relationship between energy used, work done, and the efficiency of a machine.

_____

_____

_____

_____

_____

_____

Questions 8 and 9 refer to the following information and illustration.

A structural formula of a compound shows the bonding of atoms. A molecular model shows the same thing but uses pictures of atoms rather than chemical symbols. The illustration compares the chemical formula, structural formula, and molecular model of two common compounds.

	Water	Ammonia
Chemical formula	H_2O	NH_3
Structural formula	$H - O - H$	$H - N - H$ with H below N
Molecular model (ball-and-stick type)		

8. What can you tell about a compound from a structural formula or molecular model that you cannot tell from a chemical formula?

A. which atoms are bonded to each other

B. how many atoms are in a molecule of the compound

C. the types of atoms in a compound

D. the ratio of atom types in a compound

9. What can you tell about these two compounds from the information in the table?

A. Both have isotopes.

B. Neither is an element.

C. Neither is a molecule.

D. Both are ionic compounds.

10. Anything that has mass and takes up space contains three types of subatomic particles, which are

_____, _____,

and _____.

11. The Celsius temperature scale is the one used by scientists. It is based on the freezing and boiling points of water. At 0°C, water freezes. There are 100 degrees between water's freezing and boiling points. In contrast, there are 180 degrees between the freezing and boiling points of water on the Fahrenheit scale. Which of the following is implied by the information about water and the Celsius scale?

   A. The boiling point of water is 100°C.

   B. The boiling point of water is 212°F.

   C. The freezing point of water is 32°F.

   D. The freezing point of water is below 0°C.

Type of Flour	Volume (mL)	Mass (g)	Density (g/mL)	Expected Density (g/mL)
Barley sample 1	10	4.8	0.48	0.48
Barley sample 2	10	4.7	0.47	0.48
Barley sample 3	10	4.8	0.48	0.48
Oat sample 1	10	5.1	0.51	0.52
Oat sample 2	10	5.2	0.52	0.52
Oat sample 3	10	4.8	0.48	0.52
Wheat sample 1	10	5.6	0.56	0.56
Wheat sample 2	10	5.6	0.56	0.56
Wheat sample 3	10	5.5	0.55	0.56

12. Which of the following is a chemical property of matter?

   A. how it smells

   B. how dense it is

   C. whether it is combustible

   D. whether it will break when stretched

Questions 13 and 14 refer to the following information and table.

The laboratory data in the table were recorded as a technician performed the following steps:

   (1) 10 mL of a sample was measured into a new 10 mL beaker.

   (2) The sample was poured into a clean and dry weighing pan and placed on a calibrated mass scale. The mass was recorded in the table.

   (3) The weighing pan was emptied of the sample, cleaned, and dried for reuse.

   (4) 10 mL of a new sample was measured into a new clean and dry 10 mL beaker.

   (5) The steps were completed until the samples were all processed.

   (6) The density of each sample was calculated from its mass and volume and then recorded in the table.

13. The mass and volume measurements were used to calculate density. Not all the calculations matched the expected density values. Which of the following is the most likely source of error?

   A. Some sample volumes were less than 10 milliliters.

   B. Some sample was left in the beakers during pouring into the weighing pan.

   C. The mass scale had more and more sample spilled on it as the measuring continued.

   D. Not enough samples were done for each type of flour.

14. If a 1-cup sample of each type of flour is weighed, which cup of flour will weigh the least? Why?

   _____

   _____

   _____

15. Which of these is a decomposition reaction?

   A. $C + O_2 \rightarrow CO_2$

   B. $2HgO \rightarrow 2Hg + O_2$

   C. $2Mg + O_2 \rightarrow 2MgO$

   D. $Zn + 2HCl \rightarrow ZnCl2 + H_2$

16. Balance the chemical equation.

$$P + Cl_2 \rightarrow PCl_3$$

_____

17. Is it likely that the same amount of sugar will dissolve in 20°C tea, milk, and olive oil? Explain your reasoning.

_____

_____

_____

_____

Questions 18 and 19 refer to the following graph.

Solubility of Potassium Nitrate (KNO₃)

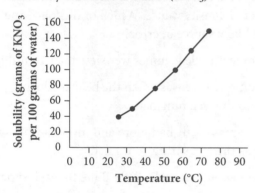

18. What is the solubility of KNO_3, measured in grams per 100 grams of water, at 58°C?

    A. 40

    B. 80

    C. 100

    D. 120

19. Suppose the temperature were lowered to 20°C. Which of these is the most likely solubility of KNO_3, in grams per 100 grams of water, at that temperature?

    A. 10

    B. 20

    C. 30

    D. 40

Question 20 refers to the following scenario.

The boiling point of pure water at sea level is tested. The water is placed in a beaker over a Bunsen burner and heated. The same thermometer is used to measure the temperature in three trials. When the water boils, the temperature is recorded. Here are the results: Trial 1: 97.6°C, Trial 2: 97.8°C, and Trial 3: 97.6°C. Since the three measurements are nearly the same, the temperature recordings can be considered accurate. However, they are more than 2 degrees lower than the accepted boiling point of pure water at sea level, which is 100°C.

20. Based on these test conditions and data, which is the best explanation for why the boiling point of water is 2 degrees below the accepted boiling point?

    A. All the temperatures were carelessly recorded.

    B. The beaker was uncovered, so heat escaped.

    C. The thermometer was slightly inaccurate.

    D. The accepted boiling point is wrong.

21. Heat is

    A. energy transferred between objects at different temperatures

    B. the thermal energy of an object's particles

    C. kinetic energy at boiling temperature

    D. the total kinetic energy of random motion

22. Convection is

    A. any movement of heat in waves rather than particles.

    B. any movement of heat from warmer to cooler particles.

    C. movement of heat from warmer to cooler particles in a solid.

    D. movement of heat from warmer to cooler particles in a liquid or gas.

23. Give an example of how heat can be used to do work.

_____

_____

_____

_____

_____

_____

_____

_____

_____

Question 24 refers to the graph below.

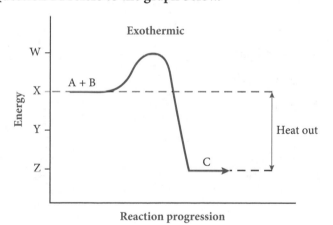

24. The activation energy in the reaction modeled by this graph is equal to

A. energy at W – energy at X

B. energy at W – energy at Z

C. energy at X – energy at Y

D. energy at X – energy at Z

25. Is energy created or destroyed in an exothermic reaction?

_____

_____

26. What are the three main types of energy?

_____

_____

_____

27. A crank flashlight, often thought of as an emergency tool or camping gear, involves many energy transformations. To work it, you turn a crank by hand, and this turns an electric coil around a magnet (or vice versa). This produces an electric current, and the current lights up the bulb when you turn the flashlight on. Identify three energy transformations and where they happen.

_____

_____

_____

_____

_____

_____

_____

_____

_____

_____

28. A chemical reaction that stores energy from the environment is called _____ thermic.

Questions 29 and 30 refer to the diagram below.

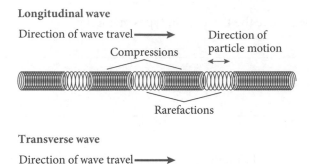

Longitudinal wave

Direction of wave travel ⟶

Direction of particle motion ⟷

Compressions

Rarefactions

Transverse wave

Direction of wave travel ⟶

Direction of particle motion ↕

29. According to the diagram, what is one of the main differences between transverse waves and longitudinal waves?

A. In longitudinal waves, particles do not move; in transverse waves, particles move a lot.

B. In longitudinal waves, energy travels in two directions; in transverse waves, it travels in one.

C. In longitudinal waves, the disturbance is in the direction of the wave energy; in transverse waves, it is not.

D. In longitudinal waves, the net particle movement is in the direction of wave travel; in transverse waves, it is not.

30. The compressions in longitudinal waves are like the crests in transverse waves. Knowing that, what can you tell about the two waves from the diagram?

A. They have the same wavelength.

B. They have different frequencies.

C. They have the same wave speed.

D. They have different amplitudes.

31. Transverse waves, but not longitudinal waves, can transmit _____ through _____.

32. Which of these is NOT a fossil fuel?

A. coal

B. natural gas

C. landfill gas

D. petroleum oil

33. Name three renewable energy sources.

_____

_____

_____

34. What energy source produces the most air pollution when it is used to generate electricity?

A. coal

B. natural gas

C. solar energy

D. uranium for nuclear fission

Unit 3: Earth and Space Science

Earth and Its Systems

Characteristics of the Atmosphere

Earth's atmosphere contains the oxygen we breathe and the carbon dioxide plants use in photosynthesis, as well as other gases. The atmosphere's five layers are quite different, as shown in the table.

The Five Layers of the Atmosphere

Layer	Temperature (°C)	Pressure (atm)	Gases	Found in this Layer
Exosphere: up to 10,000 km (6,200 miles)	(almost no particles exist to heat)	almost none	hydrogen and helium	satellites
Thermosphere: up to about 640 km (400 miles)	increases with altitude, −100 to −65	very low	almost none	beginning of "outer space," auroras, space station
Mesosphere: up to about 85 km (52 miles)	decreases with altitude, −20 to −120	decreases with altitude, 0.05 to 0	little oxygen, nitrogen, and others	meteors burning out
Stratosphere: up to about 50 km (32 miles)	increases with altitude, −60 to −20	decreases with altitude, 0.15 to 0.05	nitrogen, oxygen, ozone, and others	ozone layer, jet aircraft, weather balloons
Troposphere: up to about 18 km (11 miles)	decreases with altitude, to −60	decreases with altitude, 1 to 0.2	nitrogen, water vapor, oxygen, carbon dioxide, and others	clouds, weather, about 75% of atmospheric gases

greenhouse effect—the natural heating process of a planet by which gases in the atmosphere trap energy

The stratosphere's ozone layer absorbs some of the ultraviolet rays (wave energy) from the sun. This protects us from skin cancer and cataracts and protects plants from leaf burn. The troposphere's gases—especially carbon dioxide and water vapor—produce the **greenhouse effect**. That is, they hold in some of the sun's energy, which makes it warm enough for life on Earth—15°C on average. Compare that to the surface of Mars, which has no atmosphere and an average temperature of −30°C (that's about −20°F).

Weather and Climate

weather—the state of the atmosphere at a particular time and place

climate—the average state of the atmosphere at a particular place over many years

Our **weather** and **climate** result from the characteristics of Earth's atmosphere and the ways it interacts with land and water. Weather depends on temperature, humidity, cloud cover, precipitation, air pressure, and wind speed and direction. Climate depends on a number of things, including latitude (distance to the poles or the equator), altitude (height above sea level), and distance from large bodies of water. Increases in carbon dioxide over several decades have increased the greenhouse effect and the average temperature of Earth's troposphere, causing climate change.

Although we talk about the Atlantic and Pacific Oceans, all the ocean water on Earth is continuous. That is, there are no complete barriers, and all the oceans are actually just one ocean.

Ocean water is saltwater, so it contains sodium chloride (table salt). In addition, it contains potassium, magnesium, bromine, sulfur, and other elements, including calcium. Calcium is one of the building materials needed to make coral reefs. Coral is not an odd type of sea rock. It is the exoskeletons of coral organisms. *Exo* means "outside," and the skeletons of coral polyps are on the outsides of their bodies. Living coral reefs are large populations of coral polyps.

Wind and Currents

The oceans contribute to wind through the circulation of warm and cold water. In turn, wind contributes to ocean waves and ocean surface currents. Waves are short-term effects—their heights and wavelengths change minute to minute or hour by hour. Currents, on the other hand, are long-term movements of water over long distances.

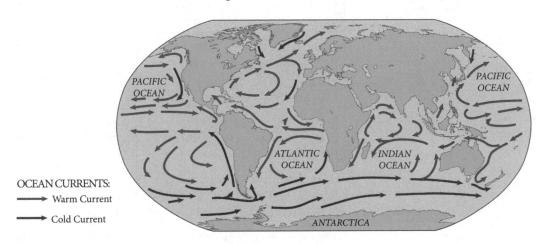

OCEAN CURRENTS:
→ Warm Current
→ Cold Current

The diagram shows several of the ocean's surface currents. Many of them were identified centuries ago, before ships had power. Sailors used the currents, along with the winds, to travel from continent to continent. But currents can be so strong that they make sailing very difficult in places. The Benguela and Agulhas currents meet at the Cape of Good Hope and make rounding the southern tip of Africa very dangerous and often deadly.

In addition to surface currents, there are deep downwelling and upwelling currents. Downwelling currents bring dissolved oxygen, produced by algae at the surface, to the bottom-dwelling marine organisms. Upwelling currents bring organic matter to the surface in large quantities. The upwelling currents near Antarctica kick-start the food web that begins with organic matter, which is eaten by krill, which is eaten by fish and other larger marine animals, which are eaten by penguins and orcas.

How Oceans Affect Climate

The combination of upward and downward currents mixes the ocean water and carries heat around the globe. This affects the temperatures of areas of water and nearby land. This is one of the ways that the ocean affects climates. Surface currents also affect climate. For example, the Gulf Stream carries heat north from the Caribbean and merges with the North Atlantic Drift. Because of those two warm currents, England has a much milder climate than many lands the same distance from the North Pole.

Interaction Between Earth's Systems

Atmosphere, ocean, land, and freshwater systems interact. One result is the different climates in different parts of the globe. Other results are winds and weather. Earth's surface and atmosphere heat unevenly, and this causes differences in air pressure. Air naturally moves from an area of high pressure to an area of low pressure—that's wind. Hot air rising at the equator flows toward the poles, and cold air sinking at the poles flows toward the equator.

Wind and Weather

Wind direction is also affected by the Earth's rotation on its axis. In areas below 30° latitude (south of New Orleans), air moving toward the equator is pushed west by the Earth's spin. Above 30° latitude, like most of the United States, air moving toward a pole is pushed east. The major winds in this country blow east and are called *prevailing westerlies*. (Winds are named for the direction they come from.)

The results of prevailing and local winds and their interactions with water are air masses. You may have seen air mass diagrams on TV. Some weather maps have red and blue curves for warm and cold fronts. When different types of air masses meet, they form a front. A cold front occurs when a cold polar air mass moves under a warm tropical air mass. A warm front occurs when a warm air mass rises over a cold air mass. The area along a front usually has unsettled weather, with clouds and precipitation (rain or snow).

Weathering and Erosion

weathering—the breaking down or dissolving of earth materials such as rock

erosion—the moving of weathered rock and soil particles by wind, water, and ice

Despite its name, **weathering** does not always depend on weather. Much weathering is done by moving water. The power of moving water is obvious during a flood—massive trees, chunks of blacktop, and even buildings are carried along by the water and deposited on riverbanks, sometimes far from where they started. Even in nonflood conditions, moving water constantly breaks off tiny particles of rock. This is weathering.

After weathering comes **erosion**—the moving of the particles. In a river, particles are pushed downstream by the water's force. When the water hits a bend or slows down, it leaves particles behind. This is deposition. Weathering and erosion make canyons, and deposition makes deltas and adds soil to floodplains.

In addition to moving water, wind also weathers and erodes rock. Sandstone outcrops in the Grand Canyon (pillars of rock surrounded by flat ground) are typical of wind-weathered rock. The Grand Canyon itself is an example of water-weathered rock. Usually, wind and water together (along with temperature changes, salts, and plants) break down rock in a process called *mechanical weathering*.

Earth is a rocky planet, unlike the gas planets in the outer solar system. But it isn't totally solid, and it changes from center to surface:

Inner core—The very center of Earth is called the *inner*, or solid, *core*. It is mostly iron and extremely hot (about 4,300°C). The radius of the inner core is about 20% of the radius of Earth.

Outer core—Around the solid core is the outer, or fluid, core. Like the inner core, it is mostly iron (plus some nickel and sulfur). It is extremely hot but cooler than the inner core (about 3,700°C). It is about twice as thick as the inner core.

Mantle—Surrounding the fluid core is the mantle, which is thicker than the fluid core and cooler (about 1,000°C). It is soft rock made up of iron and other elements (including aluminum, magnesium, oxygen, and silicon). A thin outer layer of the mantle is called the *asthenosphere*. It is very plastic; that is, it behaves almost like a fluid.

Crust—The top layer of the Earth is the crust, which is very thin compared with the other layers. It is made up of aluminum, calcium, silicon, and sodium in rock, sediments, and soil.

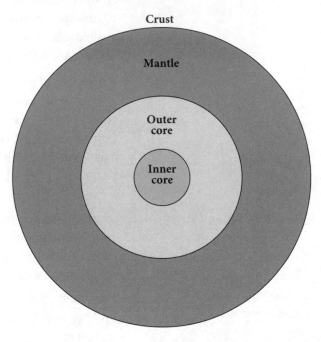

Plate Tectonics

plate tectonics—a scientific theory that describes the large-scale motion of the plates of Earth's surface

The surface of the Earth moves. The top part of the mantle—the asthenosphere—plus the crust make up a moving layer that is divided into a number of tectonic plates. Heat moving outward from Earth's core causes the tectonic plates to move around on Earth's surface, though very slowly. At one time, all Earth's continents were part of one landmass, which today we call *Pangaea*. It contained all the tectonic plates. They have been moving apart and together and apart again for billions of years, into the positions they have today.

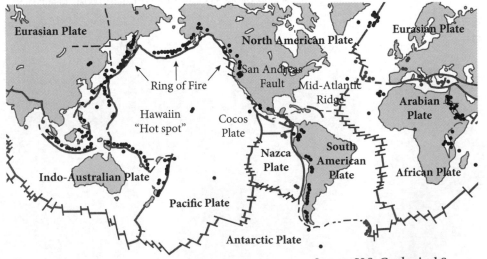

Source: U.S. Geological Survey

The Earth's tectonic plates are still moving. Some slip under other plates, and others push together, with both edges moving upward. Some plates slide past each other, and others separate. Most landform building is at tectonic plate boundaries or is associated with them.

Mountains and Volcanoes

Where two tectonic plates move toward each other, either the edges of both plates crumble, or one plate slides under the other. When continental (land) plates move together, the edges push against each other and move upward as they crumble. The process is too slow to see, but we can see the results. The Himalayas, which form the border between India and Tibet, have been built during 50 million years of collision. India was once south of its present position, on a tectonic plate moving north. When it rammed into the Eurasian plate, it slowed down. But it's still moving, and the Himalayas are still building. Today, their tallest point is Mount Everest, the tallest mountain on Earth at 8,848 meters high.

The Appalachian Mountains in North America were formed by the same process about 300 million years ago. After they formed, the tectonic plates changed direction. Then, the Appalachians were eroded by glaciers, wind, and water. What were once mountains as tall as the Himalayas are now, at their tallest, about 2,000 meters high.

On the ocean floor, tectonic plates move differently because the crust is denser than on continental plates. When two oceanic plates merge, the edge of one plate slides under the other, and a deep trench is formed. When an oceanic plate hits a continental plate, the oceanic plate slides under the continental plate. As the edge of the plate moves farther under the surface, the rock gets extremely hot and melts. Eventually, it erupts in volcanoes. You can see on the map that volcanoes form along the edges of tectonic plates. The Ring of Fire in the Pacific Ocean surrounds much of the Pacific Plate.

Rift Valleys, Mid-ocean Ridges, and Faults

Where two continental plates move apart, valleys like the Rio Grande Valley in North America are formed. Volcanoes form in rift valleys where magma (molten rock) moves up to fill the gaps in the Earth's crust. Hot springs, and sometimes geysers, occur where groundwater is heated by the magma.

On the ocean floor, spreading makes mid-ocean ridges like the Mid-Atlantic Ridge. It stretches from Iceland to the southern tip of Africa. This sea-floor spreading has been continuous for more than 100 million years.

Where tectonic plates slide past each other (at faults), their boundaries build up pressure as they bend. When they suddenly "snap" into new positions, the pressure moves in waves—earthquakes—through the Earth. This has been happening along the 800-mile San Andreas Fault for 15 million years. The Pacific Plate, on the west, moves northwest along the North American Plate, which moves southeast. The 1906 earthquake in San Francisco separated two sections of a road by 21 feet when the plates jumped.

Remember that Earth's tectonic plates have been moving for billions of years. In fact, Earth is more than 4 billion years old. The scientific evidence that tells us the age of Earth is found in radiometric measurements and in examining landforms and fossils.

Radiometric Dating

The atoms of one element all have the same number of protons, but the number of neutrons can vary. Atoms of the same element that have different numbers of neutrons are are called *isotopes*. For example, carbon has three isotopes, including carbon-14, which has two extra neutrons. Carbon-14 and some other isotopes undergo radioactive decay. That is, some subatomic particles are lost, and one isotope becomes a different isotope.

The behavior of any given isotope (one atom) is random, but a group of isotopes (a large number of the same type of atom) will have an average radioactive decay rate. So, in a group of carbon-14 atoms (all with 6 protons and 8 neutrons), half of them will decay to nitrogen-14 (7 protons and 7 neutrons) in about 5,730 years. But we don't have to wait that long to use this information. Instead, that amount of time, called the **half-life** of carbon-14, can be used with specialized equipment to find the age of something that has carbon in it. (And remember, all living things contain carbon.) This is called *radiometric dating*. Using carbon-14 and other radioactive isotopes with known half-lives, scientists have measured the ages of many different rocks in many different places in order to determine Earth's age.

> **half-life**—the time required for half of a sample of a radioactive isotope to decay into different isotopes

Landforms and Fossils

Rock on Earth's surface is newer than rock deep inside Earth. That's because new rock is continuously deposited on top. When volcanoes erupt, their lava cools and becomes rock. New rock also forms as a result of weathering and erosion of old rock, as deposited particles become stuck together over time.

Scientists have drilled as much as 2,000 meters below the ocean floor to get the oldest rock samples they can. They even hope someday to drill through Earth's crust and into the mantle. In the meantime, because tectonic plate movement and erosion have changed the earliest rock within reach, scientists have studied space rocks—moon rocks, asteroids, and meteorites (meteors that reach Earth). Thanks to radiometric dating of the deepest Earth rock samples recovered so far, as well as dating of rocks from outer space, scientists have determined that Earth is over 4 billion years old.

Radiometric dating has also been used with fossils, so we know when extinct species like dinosaurs lived on Earth. When these fossils are found in rock formations, they shed more light on the history and age of Earth.

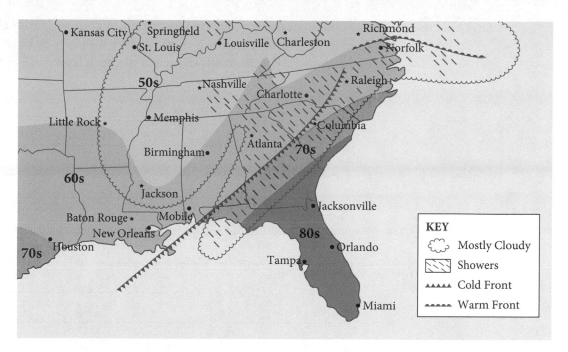

Sample Question

The prevailing winds in most areas of the United States are westerlies. Using that information and the map, predict the weather for the next several hours. Which city is most likely to see a cold air mass move under a warm air mass by tomorrow?

A. Norfolk

B. Columbia

C. Little Rock

D. Birmingham

Think It Through

Hint: Read the key to see what symbol indicates a cold air mass (cold front). Then look for that pattern on the map.

Q: What is the question asking?

A: It asks you to predict tomorrow's weather using the map.

Q: Which of the cities is near an approaching cold front?

A: Since the winds come from the west, look at the map to see which city is to the east of a cold front.

Choice A is incorrect because a warm front is leaving Norfolk.

Choice B is correct. A cold front is approaching Columbia.

Choices C and D are incorrect because Little Rock and Birmingham are not near fronts.

Sample Question

Sometimes during mountain formation, large areas of rock are tipped upward or even over. Scientists might not be sure whether the top rock layers in an area are the youngest. Assuming there are fossils in some of the rock layers, what can the scientists do to determine which layers are oldest?

_____

_____

_____

_____

_____

_____

_____

Think It Through

Hint: Take about 10 minutes to read and respond to each short-answer question. Check your writing to make sure your answer is complete.

Q: What is the question asking?

A: It asks you to explain how scientists can tell which layers of rock in a mountain are the oldest.

Q: What process can scientists use to tell the age of rocks?

A: The question tells you to assume that there are fossils in some rock layers, so scientists can use radiometric dating.

Sample answer: They can use radiometric dating with C-14 to determine the ages of some samples of the fossils. Because all living things contain carbon, all fossils contain carbon isotopes. The rock layers with the oldest fossils will be the oldest layers.

Interactions Between Living and Nonliving Things

All organisms have needs, including water, food, and air. To meet these needs, organisms use natural resources, often changing those resources in the process. Water, like many resources, moves through a natural cycle. Since most of Earth's water is in the ocean, let's start there.

The Water Cycle

Ocean water is saltwater, but when water evaporates from the ocean, the salts are left behind. In evaporation, liquid water becomes water vapor. Water vapor stays in the air until conditions cause it to condense into tiny water droplets. These make up clouds, where the water droplets may combine to form larger raindrops or freeze to form snowflakes or ice.

Clouds can travel long distances, so water molecules evaporated from the ocean may be over land when conditions cause precipitation—rain, snow, or ice. If the water falls back into the ocean, it may spend time in a marine creature before it returns to the ocean. If it falls on land, it may spend time in a land animal or plant. But first, it will fall into a pond or lake, soak into the ground, or rush down a hill to join other water molecules in rivers that eventually return to the ocean.

The water in rivers, lakes, snow, ice, and in the ground is fresh water. Land animals and plants need fresh water, but it is only 2.5 percent of the water on Earth. Much of it becomes polluted and unusable during its interactions with living things. And as the human population increases, the amount of fresh water stays the same. Fresh water is becoming scarce in some parts of the world.

The Carbon Cycle

Plants take carbon from the air and water (usually from the soil) and use energy from the sun to make sugars (carbohydrates). The plants use the sugars to make plant parts. Animals (including humans) eat parts of plants to get sugars to make animal body parts,

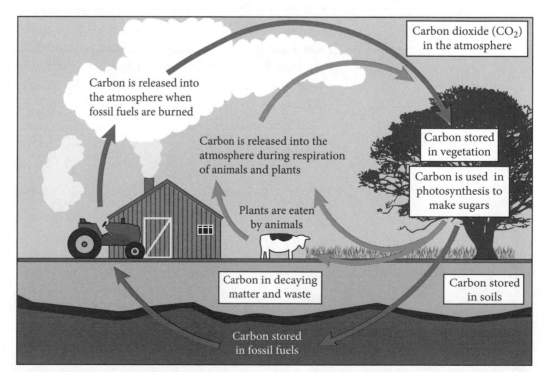

or they eat other animals for the same purpose. Carbon atoms get exchanged in various chemical reactions, and some become part of very large molecules like DNA.

Eventually, the carbon atoms return to the soil or water when dead organisms and wastes are broken down. Other carbon atoms are returned to the air during respiration. Some carbon stays in plants (such as large trees) for many years. Some remains in the soil and in rocks. Although not shown, a similar carbon cycle involving algae and sea animals occurs in the ocean. A lot of carbon remains in the ocean and in the ocean floor.

Fossil Fuels

Some of the carbon stored in rock is from plants and animals that lived millions of years ago. Under conditions of great pressure and heat, this carbon became coal, oil, or natural gas. These are the fossil fuels, named after the fossil organisms from which they were formed.

We remove and use these fossil fuels to meet our needs. We burn fossil fuels to release their energy for use in cars, in power plants, and for heat, among other things. Burning them releases carbon into the air. For centuries, plants and algae made sugars with carbon released by fossil fuel combustion, and the cycle continued. But now the plants can't use all the carbon dioxide released, and it is building up in the atmosphere.

Gases in the Earth's troposphere, especially carbon dioxide and water vapor, produce the greenhouse effect. They hold in some of the sun's energy, making it warm enough for life on Earth. With increased carbon dioxide in the atmosphere, more of the sun's energy is being held in, and the Earth is getting warmer. As the temperature rises, more snow and ice melt. Their white surfaces are no longer here to reflect some of the sun's energy back to space, so Earth gets even warmer. Scientists worldwide believe that the global temperature change is causing climate change in many areas. Results include more droughts in some areas while others have more floods, and many areas are experiencing more storms or increased storm intensity.

Other problems are caused by our use of fossil fuels. Burning coal, especially, releases sulfur into the atmosphere, where it reacts with water and becomes an acid. This contributes to acid precipitation, which weathers marble in buildings and statues and can erode metal in cars and bridges. Acid precipitation became a big problem in the 1970s when lakes far from pollution sources became so acidic that fish died. The cause, at least in part, was sulfur carried 1,000 miles by winds. Acid precipitation and climate change are good reasons for developing clean and sustainable energy technology.

Extraction and Use of Natural Resources

renewable resources—resources that can be replaced naturally in a short time

We extract fossil fuels, gold, diamonds, uranium, and water from rock. We extract peat from below the surface of the soil and trees from above the surface. We extract fish from the ocean and oxygen from the air. Some of those things are **renewable resources**. They can be replaced when they are used. Some are nonrenewable resources—they can be used up. Coal, oil, natural gas, and uranium are nonrenewable resources, yet those are what we have used most for heat and power generation.

Sustainability

sustainability—use of a resource so that it is not damaged or depleted

Sustain means to continue, or to cause to continue. How long can we sustain our use of natural resources? Or, how long can natural resources sustain us? **Sustainability** is a word that is heard more frequently as we realize that we've been using some nonrenewable resources too quickly.

Fossil fuel use is not sustainable. Not only will fossil fuels not be replaced quickly (or even in a million years), but they also cause other problems. Fossil fuel combustion contributes to air pollution, interfering with our use of air. It also contributes to climate change, interfering with our use of the land and all its resources. The process of extraction itself causes problems: Extracting oil can lead to oil spills. Extracting gas can lead to water pollution. And extracting coal can lead to mountain and forest destruction. There are other choices.

Renewable Energy Sources

Here are some renewable resources:

Biomass energy—Peat is a plant that grows in wetlands called *bogs*. It can be dried and used to improve garden soil (as peat moss). It can also be dried and used as fuel. Peat is a popular heating fuel where it grows, such as in England. Wood heat is popular in the forests of the Appalachian Mountains. Trees can be harvested sustainably through selective cutting and use of fallen wood. Some farmers grow corn used to make ethanol to replace gasoline. Refuse, such as yard wastes, can also be used as a fuel.

Wind power—Wind turbines can be placed on land or offshore. Most are huge windmills, with blades up to 40 meters long. Smaller ones can be placed on roofs in cities. As the wind turns a turbine's rotor, it turns the shaft of an electric generator.

Hydroelectric power—Hydroelectric power generation is similar to wind-powered electric generation. Flowing water turns turbine rotors, which turn the shafts of generators. This can be a practical energy source on large rivers.

Geothermal energy—Much of the energy used in San Francisco comes from water heated by Earth at the San Andreas Fault. Iceland, which sits above the Mid-Atlantic Ridge, also generates electricity and heats buildings with the heat and steam available at tectonic plate boundaries.

Solar energy—The gold standard of sustainable energy, solar heat can be collected passively with use of the right building materials. It can also be collected actively by photovoltaic cells to generate electricity.

Natural Hazards

derechos—large clusters of thunderstorms that produce damaging straight-line winds

According to the National Weather Service, approximately 100,000 thunderstorms, 1,000 tornadoes, and 2 hurricanes hit the United States every year. Flooding, **derechos**, lightning strikes, snow, and ice are all results of various kinds of storms. We can't prevent them, but we can prepare for them. News stations and NOAA Weather Radio broadcast disaster watches and warnings based on satellite data. Some communities have alarms or sirens or use telephone alerts. Warnings give people time to evacuate or seek shelter before disasters. Following building codes and building home storm shelters are other ways to reduce damage. The table provides information about some of the natural hazards that occur.

Natural Hazard	Effects	Mitigation	Frequency
Earthquake: seismic waves through the Earth	toppled buildings and bridges, broken gas and electric lines	building codes that require earthquake-resistant construction	frequent, although earthquakes strong enough to be felt or cause damage are infrequent
Hurricane: tropical storm with circling winds of 74 mph	toppled trees and buildings, flooding, habitat destruction	warnings, dikes, evacuation plans, storm shelters	semifrequent during summer and fall along Gulf and Atlantic Coasts
Tornado: column of fast-rotating air touching the ground	toppled and displaced trees and buildings	warnings, storm shelters	frequent with thunderstorms in flat areas
Forest fire: burning of extended forest area	burned buildings and trees, wildlife and habitat destruction	evacuation plans	unpredictable, caused by people or lightning strikes
Drought: long period with much less than normal precipitation	crop failure, water shortages	water conservation and rationing	becoming more common with climate change

Hurricanes, tornadoes, and derechos involve strong winds that can blow over trees, buildings, and vehicles and cause deaths and injuries. Hurricanes and heavy rainstorms cause flooding that can destroy habitat and have other long-term effects. Power outages are caused by storms with high winds and also by blizzards and ice storms. Snow can cause roofs to collapse, snow and ice can lead to traffic accidents, and blizzards can cover food for so long that wildlife starves.

Earth movements cause tsunamis, volcanoes, and earthquakes. Tsunamis are sea waves caused by an earthquake or other disturbances on the ocean floor. A tsunami may not be noticeable in the ocean but can be deadly to islands and coasts. The wave transfers a lot of energy and moves every thing, animal, and person it hits on land, drowning many. Volcanoes can erupt, sometimes without much warning, when magma moves upward through Earth's crust. Lava reaches temperatures around 1,000°C and burns everything in its path. Volcanic smoke, which is acidic, is hazardous to breathe. Volcanic ash clouds reduce air temperatures and drift around the globe. Earthquakes are hard to predict, but new engineering that allows buildings to sway rather than crack reduces damage in fault zones.

Guided Practice

Sample Question   All but one of the following actions are caused by our burning fossil fuels for energy. Which action is NOT the result of fossil fuel use?

A. carbon buildup in the atmosphere

B. droughts caused by climate change

C. sulfur pollution that causes acid precipitation

D. great pressure and heat underground

Think It Through

Hint: Read the options. Eliminate the incorrect answers.

Q: What is the question asking?

A: It asks which action is not caused by our use of fossil fuels.

Choices A, B, and C are incorrect because they are all caused by the use of fossil fuels.

Choice D is correct. Great pressure and heat underground are conditions that led to the making of fossil fuels.

Sample Question   Which of these natural disasters is hardest to predict in terms of time (not location)?

A. earthquake

B. hurricane

C. tornado

D. drought

Think It Through

Q: What is the question asking?

A: It asks which of the natural disasters listed is hardest to predict when it will happen.

Q: How is each of the disasters predicted?

A: Read each choice, and think about how you would predict when it might occur.

Choice A is correct. It's easy to predict *where* earthquakes will happen—near tectonic plate boundaries. But *when* they will happen is unpredictable.

Choices B, C, and D are incorrect because weather reports can help predict when they are likely to occur.

The universe consists of all matter, radiation, and the space in between. No one is sure how the universe was created, but one widely accepted theory is called the *big bang*. According to this theory, the universe was created as a result of an explosion about 13.7 billion years ago. Originally, it was extremely dense and smaller than an atomic particle. This object began to expand rapidly, forming particles of matter and eventually stars and galaxies. Microwave background radiation coming from all corners of the universe provides evidence to support the big bang theory. Scientists think this radiation was released when the universe first expanded.

There are several models that predict what will happen to the universe in the future.

- In the *open* universe model, the universe will continue to expand indefinitely. Its density will decrease over time.
- In the *closed* universe model, the universe will expand, slow down, stop, and then begin to contract.
- In the *balanced* universe model, gravity will slow expansion until a stable state is reached.
- In the *oscillating* universe model, the universe will collapse, and gravity will pull all matter back to the center. Eventually, the universe will expand again in another big bang.

Galaxies

A galaxy is a collection of billions of stars. Earth's galaxy, the Milky Way, is just one of hundreds of billions of galaxies in the universe. Galaxies are classified by their shapes. A spiral galaxy has a dense center of billions of stars and arms that spiral out from the center. Older stars are located in the center. Younger stars are located in the spiral arms. The Milky Way is a spiral galaxy. Our sun is located in one of its spiral arms. A barred spiral galaxy has a straight bar of stars across the center. The spiral arms extend from the end of the bars. Elliptical galaxies are oval shaped. They consist mainly of old stars. Irregular galaxies have no particular shape or arrangement of stars. Most of the stars in irregular galaxies are young.

Constellations

Constellations are groups of stars as seen from Earth. They have been used for centuries to navigate. One of the best-known constellations, the Big Dipper, is always in the northern sky and can be used to locate the North Star, Polaris. The other constellations circle around the North Star.

Stars

Hydrogen and other gases and dust in the universe collect into a cloud called a stellar nebula. It begins to contract because of gravity. That is, each particle is attracted to each other particle, depending on its size and their distance from each other. The closer they get, the more they pull on each other. More particles join the rotating nebula, and it becomes more dense. When it gains enough mass, it reaches the protostar stage (*proto* means "beginning"). Thermonuclear fusion of hydrogen to helium begins. This releases heat and light, and a star is born. What we see as a point of sparkling light is a mass of plasma and gas that gives off ultraviolet light, X-rays, and other wavelengths of electromagnetic energy.

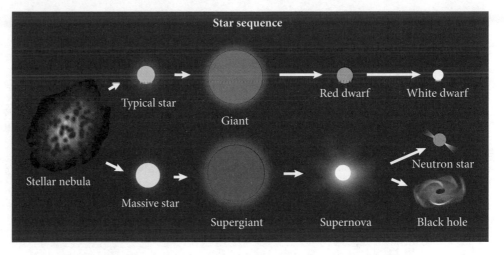

Star sequence

Stellar nebula — Typical star — Giant — Red dwarf — White dwarf
Massive star — Supergiant — Supernova — Neutron star — Black hole

luminosity—the brightness of a star

As the fusion process becomes more stable, 90 percent of stars become average, or main-sequence, stars. Early in their existence, stars are hot and massive and have more **luminosity** than the sun. In the middle of the sequence, fusion reactions are stable, and the stars lose mass gradually over billions of years. Our sun is a middle-sequence star. Scientists expect it to last another 10 billion years. Some stars at this stage become giants, like Pollux. Later in the sequence, thermonuclear fusion has changed most of the hydrogen into helium. The stars become less massive and less luminous and may become red **dwarfs** and finally white dwarfs. Theoretically, they then become black dwarfs and give off no light.

dwarf—a star with low to average luminosity, mass, and size

Star Traits

About 10 percent of the stars in the universe are not main-sequence stars. These go through a different sequence of changes. As the diagram shows, very massive stars may become bright supergiants. Thousands of times larger than the sun, they don't last as long as main-sequence stars. At the end of their cycle, massive stars may explode as supernovas and then become neutron stars. Or they may become black holes—spaces around matter with so much gravity that even light can't get out.

A large percentage of stars are in binary systems—they are pairs of stars. Scientists thank that half the stars in the universe may be in binary systems. At least some of these star pairs have planets orbiting them. Alpha Centauri A and B are binary stars.

You may have noticed that some stars look reddish or bluish, while others seem yellow or white. Color is related to temperature. Very hot stars are blue. As their temperatures decrease, the stars' colors go through white and then yellow and orange to red, which is the color of the coolest stars.

Within the Milky Way galaxy is our solar system. It is made up of one star—our sun—and the various objects that orbit it. Gravity, the same force that makes particles condense into protostars, formed the solar system and causes the planets and other objects to orbit the sun. The sun contains more than 99 percent of the solar system's mass. The planets in our solar system are characterized as rocky or gaseous.

Rocky Planets

Mercury is the closest planet to the sun and the smallest of the rocky planets. It is about the size of our moon and orbits the sun in 88 days. Mercury has a thin atmosphere, with no moons or rings.

Venus, the second planet, is about Earth's size and has no moons or rings. It is blanketed in clouds and has an atmosphere made mostly of carbon dioxide. This gas traps heat, making the planet's surface almost 480°C.

Earth's surface is mainly water. Because of its distance from the sun and protective atmosphere, surface temperatures do not reach the extremes of the other planets. It is the only place in the solar system where life is known to exist. Earth has one natural satellite, the moon.

Mars, the fourth planet, is smaller than Earth and has two small moons. Its red color comes from iron oxide (rust) in the soil. Rust is a product of the chemical reaction between iron and water, hinting that Mars had liquid water at one time. It does have frozen water now in its small polar ice caps.

Gaseous Planets

The four outer planets are mostly made up of gases, but three of the four have solid cores. Jupiter, the fifth and largest planet, is mostly made of hydrogen and helium gases. Its main feature is the Great Red Spot, a large revolving cloud of gases. It has at least 50 moons and a faint ring system.

Saturn, the sixth planet, is circled by many rings. These rings are made up of billions of icy particles, some the size of dust and some the size of mountains. There are also two small moons between rings. The rings orbit at different speeds. Saturn is not thought to have a solid core.

Uranus is the seventh planet. It contains more methane than Jupiter or Saturn, which gives it a bluish color. It is also different in that its equator goes from north to south. That is, it is at a right angle to the equators of the other planets. Uranus has a faint ring system and 27 moons.

Neptune, the eighth planet, is bluish like Uranus, also because of its methane. It is 30 times farther from the sun than Earth is, and it takes 165 Earth years to orbit the sun once. It has 13 or more moons and six rings.

dwarf planet—a round celestial body that is not a moon, orbits the sun, and has not cleared the path around its orbit

Beyond Neptune are several **dwarf planets**. The most well known is Pluto, which was considered the ninth planet of our solar system until 2006. Dwarf planets are solid (rocky or icy). They are smaller than Earth's moon but may have moons of their own. They do not have rings.

Comets, Asteroids, and Meteors

Asteroids and comets also revolve around the sun. Most asteroids are in the asteroid belt between Mars and Jupiter. Asteroids are solid but much smaller than rocky planets. In fact, the combined mass of all asteroids is smaller than the mass of Earth's moon. Asteroids have no atmospheres and cannot support life.

Comets are relatively small icy bodies orbiting the sun. Short-period comets are in the Kuiper Belt (a region of space beyond Neptune), along with many dwarf planets. Long-period comets have unpredictable orbits and come from the Oort Cloud, a vast distance away. When these comets approach the sun, they heat up. Gases and dust are released, forming a tail millions of kilometers long behind the icy, rocky core. The most famous comet is probably Halley's Comet, which orbits the sun once every 76 years.

Meteors, which we see as shooting stars, are rocky "space debris." Some are bits of comet tails. They are called *meteoroids* when they are in space, *meteors* when they enter Earth's atmosphere, and *meteorites* if they don't burn out before they hit the ground. Their bright trails are particles that break off because of the force of friction against the Earth's air particles. The friction also increases their energy until they light up.

Tides, Phases, and Eclipses

The relative positions of the sun, moon, and Earth explain the tides. Because of gravity, both sun and moon pull on the ocean's water. When both are on the same side of Earth, the pull is greatest. We get the highest high tides on one side of Earth and the lowest low tides on the other. When Earth is between the sun and moon, the sun's gravity decreases the effect of the moon's, and the difference in the tides isn't as dramatic.

Relative positions also partly explain the phases of the moon. Other contributors to what we see as phases include the facts that the moon reflects sunlight and that we can only see the side of the moon that faces the sun. When we see a gibbous or crescent moon, it's because we see only part of the side of the moon that is exposed to sunlight.

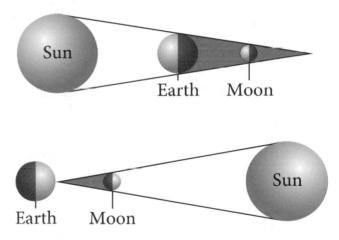

As the diagram shows, the relative positions of Earth, the moon, and the sun also cause eclipses. When Earth is directly between the sun and the moon, there is a lunar eclipse on the moon (dark) side of Earth. When the moon is directly between Earth and the sun, people in a small area of the daylight side of Earth will experience a solar eclipse.

Sample Question When does a lunar eclipse occur?

A. when the moon comes between Earth and the sun

B. when Earth comes between the sun and the moon

C. when the sun's shadow falls across Earth

D. when the moon's shadow falls across the sun

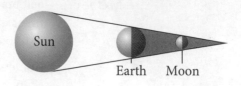

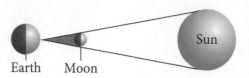

Think It Through

Q: What is the question asking?

A: It asks what happens when a lunar eclipse occurs.

Q: What is a lunar eclipse?

A: When Earth is between the sun and the moon, Earth's shadow blocks the moon.

Choice A is incorrect because when the moon is between Earth and the sun, there is a solar eclipse.

Choice B is correct. A lunar eclipse occurs when Earth comes between the sun and the moon.

Choices C and D are incorrect because the sun never casts a shadow nor has a shadow cast on it.

Sample Question A _____ eclipse can be seen on more places on Earth than a _____ eclipse when Earth, the sun, and the moon are aligned.

Think It Through

Hint: Look carefully at both diagrams. Imagine yourself in different places on Earth.

Q: What is the question asking?

A: It asks which type of eclipse can be seen in more places than the other.

Q: In which diagram is the shadow visible to a larger part of Earth?

A: During a lunar eclipse, when the moon is in shadow, the shadow is seen in more places on Earth.

A **lunar** eclipse can be seen on more places on Earth than a **solar** eclipse when Earth, the sun, and the moon are aligned.

Questions 1 and 2 refer to the following map.

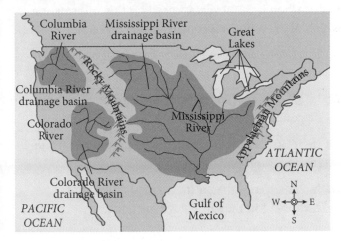

1. What landform is most likely to be a result of one tectonic plate slipping under another tectonic plate?

   A. Great Lakes

   B. Gulf of Mexico

   C. Rocky Mountains

   D. Colorado River drainage basin

2. Drainage basins, or watersheds, are areas of land where all the surface water drains toward a river. Which of the following is one cause for the Mississippi River drainage basin?

   A. Tectonic plates met and built mountains to its east and west.

   B. Water runs from north to south in the Northern Hemisphere.

   C. Water collects where tectonic plates slide past each other.

   D. Hot springs form where magma heats groundwater.

3. What are coral reefs made of?

   _____

   _____

   _____

4. A meteorologist wants to study climate change in Alaska. What data would provide the most accurate information on climate change in that state?

   A. temperature and humidity data for Alaska over the past 10 years

   B. precipitation and air pressure data for Alaska over the past 100 years

   C. precipitation and air pressure conditions in the troposphere over the current year

   D. temperature and precipitation conditions in the troposphere over the past 10 years

5. Name two characteristics of weather and two conditions that influence climate. Explain the major difference between weather and climate.

   _____

   _____

   _____

   _____

   _____

   _____

   _____

   _____

6. A very dry desert exists along the west coast of South America. North of it, the coastal area is covered with rain forest. Which of these is the most likely cause of the climate differences along the coast?

   A. A warm surface current brings storms to the desert coast.

   B. A downwelling current takes water vapor away from the coast.

   C. An upwelling current dries the air before it blows over the desert.

   D. A cold surface current dries the air before it blows over the desert.

7. Which of the following is *least* likely to affect wind speed or direction?

    A. uneven heating of land

    B. flooding after a rainstorm

    C. differences in air pressure

    D. Earth's rotation on its axis

Questions 8 and 9 refer to the following information.

Atmospheric scientists have been observing carbon dioxide levels over several years and in different areas. They want to know how much concentrations of CO_2 have been increasing and where it is coming from. They also want to know which of Earth's features act as carbon sinks. A carbon sink involves the removal of carbon from the atmosphere and storage of carbon somewhere else. Known carbon sinks include the ocean and forests. The scientists use a number of sampling methods.

8. What is the best sampling plan for determining how well the ocean functions as a carbon sink?

    A. daily samples for a year above a likely spot in the ocean

    B. hourly samples for one day above a likely spot in the ocean

    C. daily samples for a year in many places over land and ocean

    D. hourly samples for one day in many places over land and ocean

9. Assume one of the scientists hypothesizes that a particular area of the ocean will absorb and store more carbon than average. What is the most important thing the scientist should do to test that hypothesis?

    A. compare CO_2 levels over that area with CO_2 levels over other areas

    B. compare CO_2 levels over that area in different months of many years

    C. pump carbon into the water there and take more measurements over time

    D. release carbon over the area and take more measurements there over time

10. The currently accepted value for the half-life of radiocarbon is 5,730 years. Based on this information, which of the following conclusions is correct?

    A. In 11,460 years, the entire sample will be another element.

    B. In 5,730 years, half the original sample of carbon will be gone.

    C. In 5,730 years, half the original amount of carbon-14 in the sample will be gone.

    D. In 2,865 years, the entire original amount of carbon-14 in the sample will be gone.

11. As part of the water cycle, water (which is nonliving) enters organisms and spends some time within them before returning to the environment. Explain how water enters and leaves a plant, marine animal, or land animal.

    _____

    _____

    _____

    _____

    _____

    _____

    _____

    _____

    _____

12. Which of these graphs correctly shows how CO_2 in the atmosphere has changed over the last 50 years?

A.

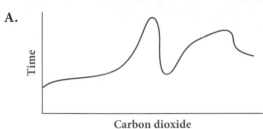

B.

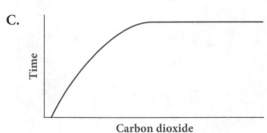

C.

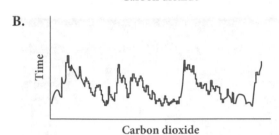

D.

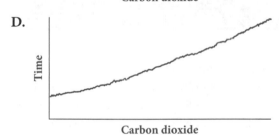

13. The temperature of the Earth's inner core is about 4,300°C, and the average temperature of the Earth's surface is about 15°C. Therefore the temperature of Earth decreases by about _____ from the middle of the inside to the outside.

Questions 14 and 15 refer to the following graph.

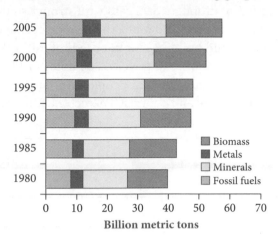

14. The graph shows the worldwide extraction of some natural resources over several recent decades. Which of the following can be learned from this graph?

  A. Extraction of gold and silver has decreased.

  B. More fossil fuels than biomass have been extracted.

  C. Less than a third of the resources extracted have been renewable.

  D. Extraction of resources almost doubled from 1980 to 2000.

15. What conclusion can you base on the data in the graph?

_____

_____

_____

_____

_____

_____

_____

_____

16. A derecho is an uncommon storm. It is a large collection of thunderstorm cells with strong "straight-line winds" of 50 to 100 mph. They knock over and move trees and buildings for hundreds of miles. A derecho in June of 2012 traveled 800 miles in 13 hours, leaving more than 4 million people without electric power. Compare and contrast a derecho with a tornado.

_____

_____

_____

_____

_____

_____

_____

_____

_____

17. Name three land materials that move between the Earth and the atmosphere. Briefly explain the three processes.

_____

_____

_____

_____

_____

_____

_____

_____

18. What type of galaxy is the Milky Way?

   A. elliptical

   B. barred spiral

   C. irregular

   D. spiral

Question 19 refers to the following diagram.

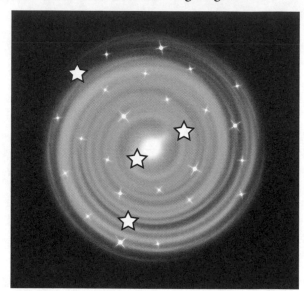

19. This is an illustration of the Milky Way galaxy as it might be seen from "above" or "below" its plane. When we see it from Earth, we are within the plane of the spiral, so we can't see the spiral arms, but on this drawing you can. Which of the stars marks the approximate real position of the sun?

   A. the one on the top left

   B. the one on the middle right

   C. the one on the middle left

   D. the one on the bottom left

20. The layer of Earth that contains the asthenosphere is the

_____

21. Which of the following is most likely to yield evidence to support one of the models of the future of the universe?

   A. analysis of different types of radiation coming from the center of Earth

   B. analysis of asteroids in the solar system data collected from planetary missions

   C. data collected from observing the arms of the Milky Way galaxy

   D. data collected from observing galaxies and clusters of galaxies of different ages

22. Sandstone outcrops in the Grand Canyon were formed by strong wind wearing away rock particles in the process of _____.

23. What are the differences between weathering, erosion, and deposition?

   _____

   _____

   _____

   _____

   _____

   _____

24. Which of these planets is most likely to experience a greenhouse effect?

   A. Mercury, which has a very thin atmosphere that is mostly oxygen

   B. Venus, which has a thick atmosphere of mostly carbon dioxide

   C. Mars, which has a thin atmosphere mostly of carbon dioxide and some dust

   D. Jupiter, which has a solid core surrounded by helium and hydrogen

25. The mesosphere is the layer of Earth's atmosphere where we usually see meteors, or shooting stars. What happens to meteors once they enter the atmosphere?

   A. Most burn out while they are in the mesosphere.

   B. Some move down into the stratosphere and fall apart.

   C. Some become meteoroids and move out into the thermosphere.

   D. Most become meteorites and move down into the troposphere.

Practice Test

Question 1 refers to the following information.

Dentists don't use silver fillings much anymore. Today, dentists use a lot of resin composites. The composite materials have been improved in recent years. Some of the early ones took a long time to harden. Others came in two parts that had to be mixed together to start a chemical reaction, which hardened the material quickly. It had to be shaped on the tooth in a hurry. With the newest composites, the dentist does not have to rush. Once the resin is correctly in place, the dentist hardens it by shining a curing light on it. The resin heats up as it hardens, and then it cools. The result is a hard material, and you can chew foods immediately.

1. What can you conclude about the chemical reaction of the newest resin composites?

   A. It takes in and gives off energy, so it is endothermic.

   B. It takes in light and gives off heat, so it is exothermic.

   C. Its activation energy is provided by heat from the light.

   D. Its activation energy is provided by light that starts the reaction.

Questions 2 and 3 refer to the following diagram.

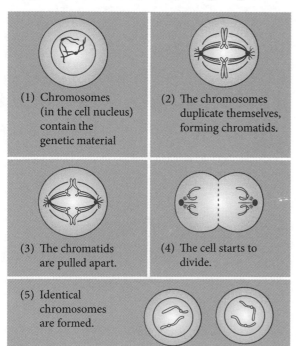

(1) Chromosomes (in the cell nucleus) contain the genetic material

(2) The chromosomes duplicate themselves, forming chromatids.

(3) The chromatids are pulled apart.

(4) The cell starts to divide.

(5) Identical chromosomes are formed.

2. What process does this diagram show?

   A. mitosis, which results in gametes

   B. meiosis, which results in gametes

   C. mitosis, which results in daughter cells

   D. meiosis, which results in daughter cells

3. During this process, 2N cells produce 2N cells. In the process in which sex cells are produced, 2N cells produce 1N (also called N) cells. What does "2N" mean?

   A. The chromosomes cross over in step 2.

   B. The cell has two copies of each component.

   C. There are two copies of each type of chromosome.

   D. The cell membrane has gone through cytokinesis two times.

Questions 4 and 5 refer to the following scenario.

During practice, a soccer ball with a mass of 400 g rolls from the left toward the center of the field, covering 5 m in 10 s. A slightly larger soccer ball, with a mass of 450 g, rolls from the right toward the center of the field, from the opposite side of the field. It is covering 4 m in 10 s. The two balls collide near the center of the field.

4. What is the speed of the larger ball?

   A. 0.4 m/s

   B. 0.4 m/s^2

   C. 4 m

   D. 10 s

5. What is most likely to happen to the two balls when they collide?

   A. They will both reverse direction at slightly different speeds.

   B. They will both go left, because the larger ball has more mass.

   C. They will both go right, because the smaller ball has more velocity.

   D. They will stop moving, because they had approximately the same momentum.

Practice Test

6. A large grassland is being developed into an area for vacation homes. Which of the following is most likely to happen to the elk that live there and eat grass and wildflowers?

   A. Most of the elk will ignore the people, and the elk population will increase.

   B. Some elk will die from lack of food, but the population will recover over time.

   C. Most of the elk will leave the area, and the population will decline permanently.

   D. Some elk will move and join another population that will increase permanently.

7. In what ways is Earth's core very different from its surface?

   _____

   _____

   _____

   _____

   _____

   _____

   _____

   _____

   _____

   _____

   _____

8. Which of the following general statements about cells is correct?

   A. Only a few types of cells need energy.

   B. Living cells can be made from chemicals.

   C. Plant and animal cells contain many of the same structures.

   D. All cells perform photosynthesis and make food using light energy.

Questions 9 and 10 refer to the information and diagram below.

Rain and melted snow seep into the ground, filling the openings in rock and sediment. The top surface of the saturated zone of rock is the water table. People draw on this water supply by digging wells, as shown here.

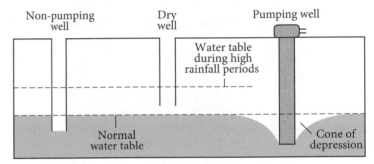

9. What probably caused the cone of depression below the pumping well?

   _____

   _____

   _____

   _____

10. What evidence supports the conclusion that the dry well was drilled during a period of abundant rainfall?

    A. It does not have a pump.

    B. This area always has abundant rainfall.

    C. The dry well was drilled before the pumping well.

    D. The dry well only reaches below the highest water table level.

Question 11 refers to the following information.

One of the following scenarios is an example of adaptation; three are not.

(A) A lion and a tiger were bred and produced a "liger." The liger expressed some lion traits and some tiger traits.

(B) Most of a population of white foxes had ancestors that were brown in a time before the area became snowier.

(C) An area had a longer than usual rainy season, rivers expanded, and individuals that could swim well survived better than others.

(D) A fence was built around an apple orchard to keep deer out. Some members of the local deer population learned where to jump the fence.

11. Which scenario provides an example of adaptation?

   A. liger traits

   B. white foxes

   C. swimming

   D. jumping fences

Questions 12–14 refer to the following information.

A staagle is a fictional mammal with the following characteristics: (1) long curly hair, (2) blue or (3) orange or (4) purple hair, and either (5) horns or (6) no horns. The numbers in parentheses each represent a single trait in the possible combination of these six staagle traits. There are six possible permutations: 1 2 5; 1 2 6; 1 3 5; 1 3 6; 1 4 5; and 1 4 6.

12. Which of the following combinations of characteristics is a possible staagle phenotype?

   A. short blue hair and horns

   B. short curly hair and no horns

   C. long orange hair and no horns

   D. long purple and blue hair and horns

13. Assume that blue is the dominant allele for hair color and that having horns is the recessive allele for the horn trait. Which of the following Punnett squares correctly shows some possible genotypes for staagles?

A.

	Blue	orange
purple	**Blue** purple	purple orange
purple	**Blue** purple	purple orange

B.

	Blue	orange
horns	**Blue** horns	orange horns
No Horns	**Blue** **No Horns**	orange **No Horns**

C.

	horns	**No Horns**
horns	horns horns	horns horns
No Horns	horns **No Horns**	**No Horns** **No Horns**

D.

	Long	**Curly**
Blue	**Long** **Blue**	Curly Blue
orange	**Long** orange	**Curly** orange

14. A staagle with a No Horns–No Horns genotype mates with a staagle with a No Horns–horns genotype. What is the probability that their first offspring will have horns?

   A. 100%

   B. 50%

   C. 25%

   D. 0%

15. After exercising for a while, you may "run out of breath." If you keep running after this point, your metabolism changes from _____ respiration to _____ respiration.

16. An ion is an atom that has an unequal number of protons and electrons, and therefore it has a positive or negative charge. A sodium atom normally has 11 protons, 11 neutrons, and 11 electrons. What would a sodium atom become if it lost an electron to another atom?

A. an isotope

B. a neutral ion

C. a positively charged ion

D. a negatively charged ion

17. Waves transmit _____.

Question 18 refers to the following information and diagram.

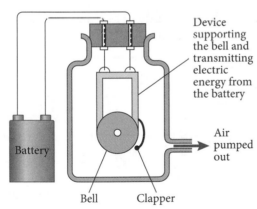

Device supporting the bell and transmitting electric energy from the battery

Air pumped out

Battery

Bell   Clapper

A bell is placed in a jar and connected to a battery so the bell rings without stopping. Air is pumped out of the jar using a vacuum pump.

18. What happens to the sound of the bell as the air is pumped out of the jar?

A. It gets louder and louder.

B. It gets quieter and quieter.

C. Its pitch gets higher as the frequency increases.

D. Its pitch gets lower as the wavelength increases.

Question 19 refers to the following information and graph.

Radioactivity results from the natural decay of an atomic nucleus. If a substance is radioactive, it gradually emits nuclear particles and forms new nuclei until it becomes stable. The half-life of a radioactive substance is the time it takes for half of the substance to decay. The radioactivity of a substance is shown below.

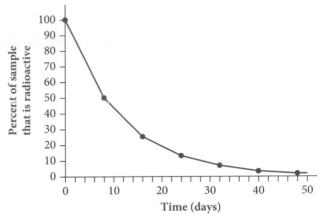

19. What is the half-life of the radioactive substance shown in the graph?

A. 8 days

B. 16 days

C. 24 days

D. 50 days

20. What is true of the products of any chemical reaction?

A. They have the same elements and properties as the reactants.

B. They have different elements than the reactants and weigh more.

C. They have different elements than the reactants but weigh the same.

D. They have the same elements as the reactants but different properties.

21. Name three routes of disease transmission.

_____

_____

_____

Practice Test

Questions 22–24 refer to the following information.

Sodium chloride is spread on roads in winter to prevent icing or to melt ice and snow that are already present. Salty water runs off into gutters and into streams. It can damage fish and other freshwater organisms. If the salt water gets into water supplies, it can be bad for people who are on low-sodium diets.

To test for sodium chloride in the environment, researchers sampled stream water near an intersection of two heavily salted roads. The sample area was a circle with a radius of 10 km. Samples were taken at 1-km distances along streams running away from the intersection. Sampling was done once a month for the three months of winter. Samples were tested for chloride and compared.

22. What would most improve the sampling technique and results?

    A. taking samples more frequently

    B. taking similar samples in the summer

    C. recording the road conditions with each sample

    D. sampling streams running toward the intersection

23. Which of these could lead to errors in the results and conclusions?

    (1) No samples of tap water were taken in the study area.

    (2) Sample containers were emptied but not washed before reuse.

    (3) The intersection was on a hill, so water ran away from the center of the area.

    (4) Some other chloride salts were used on the roads in addition to sodium chloride.

    A. 1 and 2

    B. 2 and 4

    C. 3 and 1

    D. 4 and 3

24. Which of these were weaknesses of the study design?

    (1) Samples were only compared to each other.

    (2) Samples were taken only once a month.

    (3) Road salt conditions were not recorded.

    (4) No samples were taken far from salted roads.

    A. 1 and 4

    B. 1 and 3

    C. 2 and 3

    D. 2 and 4

Questions 25 and 26 refer to the following diagram.

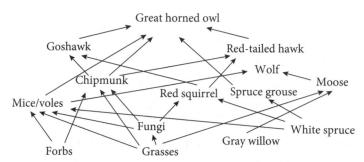

25. Which group is a member of the most food chains within this food web?

    A. chipmunks

    B. mice/voles

    C. white spruces

    D. great horned owls

26. Draw a food chain using the information in the diagram.

Practice Test

27. According to scientists, when is work done?

   A. when a task is performed

   B. when effort force is expended

   C. when a force moves an object

   D. when the mass of an object decreases

Question 28 refers to the diagram below.

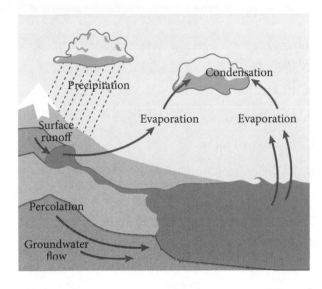

28. This diagram of the water cycle is missing at least one arrow. What new arrow is most important to make the diagram more accurate?

_____

_____

29. News agencies in Iowa reported that a number of trees and buildings had been knocked over. Was the likely cause an earthquake, hurricane, or tornado? Explain your reasoning.

_____

_____

_____

_____

_____

_____

_____

30. Suppose you have a sample of a clear liquid that looks like water. Which is the best way to determine whether the liquid is pure water without anything dissolved in it?

_____

_____

_____

_____

_____

_____

_____

31. One of these is NOT an example of transformation of energy. In which example is energy conserved in its original form?

   A. potatoes to body motion

   B. wind to electric power

   C. coal to home heat

   D. trees to lumber

Practice Test

Question 32 refers to the following diagram.

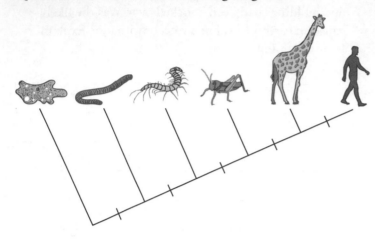

32. Examine the cladogram and consider what traits could be written at the small lines to separate the groups. Then choose the correct order of the correct traits that would separate some of the groups.

   A. lives on land; legs; fur or hair

   B. legs; six or fewer legs; two legs

   C. six or fewer legs; fur or hair; high intelligence

   D. multicellular; no more than six legs; two legs

33. Which of the following occurs as a muscle protein is made?

   A. A gene makes a chromosome, which makes a muscle protein.

   B. Information carried by DNA is transcribed to make a muscle protein.

   C. Each DNA base is translated into an amino acid that helps make up muscle.

   D. A muscle protein translates a chromosome into genes that make amino acids.

34. When is a solution saturated?

   A. when the solute is a gas

   B. when the solute is a liquid

   C. when the solute cannot be seen

   D. when no more solute will dissolve

35. Which of the following statements about heating a material is true?

   A. Heat rises in solid materials.

   B. In conduction, the particles stay in one place.

   C. Radiation happens in air as well as in liquid materials.

   D. In convection, particles do not have to touch each other.

36. During the last stage of a star's sequence, what determines the form it will take?

   A. its age

   B. its brightness

   C. its original mass

   D. its fusion reactions

37. Changes in what a species eats, the size of its individuals, and where they live are characteristic of

   A. selective breeding.

   B. ecological divergence.

   C. reproductive isolation.

   D. ·variation of genetic traits.

38. What scientific evidence supports the understanding that Earth is more than 4 billion years old?

   _____

   _____

   _____

   _____

   _____

   _____

39. Compare and contrast a moon with an asteroid.

_____

_____

_____

_____

_____

_____

_____

_____

_____

_____

Question 40 refers to the following information.

Animals and plants have many ways of maintaining homeostasis. Three of the following examples of behavior or function maintain biological homeostasis, but one does not.

(1) The albatross and other marine birds have salt glands, near the nostrils in most species, that let extra salt out of their bodies. These birds can drink salt water because salt is removed from their body fluids when there is too much.

(2) Ectotherms (cold-blooded animals), such as snakes and lizards, often turn themselves sideways to the sun to collect more heat when they need it. They also lie with their heads toward the sun (parallel to the sun's rays) to reduce the heat they collect when they're hot, or they seek out shade.

(3) Male bowerbirds collect objects such as blue bottle caps and then decorate their territories with them to attract female bowerbirds. Other males sometimes steal these objects. When this happens, the bowerbirds replace the stolen objects with new ones to keep the territory at its best.

(4) Plants lose water through their stomata (pores) when they transpire. When there is enough water in the soil, the plants take in water through their roots to replace what they lose to the atmosphere.

40. Which example does NOT maintain biological homeostasis?

A. 1

B. 2

C. 3

D. 4

Questions 41 and 42 refer to the following scenario and table.

You need a small bit of material with a lot of weight, but it has to be a material that is easy to get. You decide to compare several materials that you already have. First, you prepare a sample of each material, all to the same dimensions—1-cm cubes. Then you measure each one separately and record your measurements (without units). Here is the resulting data:

A	B	C	D	E	F
1.7	2.3	2.7	1.5	9.0	7.8

41. Given the information you had, what measurement did you decide to take?

A. mass

B. weight

C. density

D. volume

42. What is the mean of your measurements?

A. 1.5

B. 9.0

C. 2.5

D. 4.2

Questions 43 and 44 refer to the following diagram.

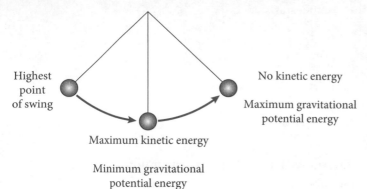

Highest point of swing

No kinetic energy

Maximum gravitational potential energy

Maximum kinetic energy

Minimum gravitational potential energy

43. At what point in the swing is the ball moving the fastest?

 A. at the bottom

 B. at the top left

 C. above the top left

 D. just below the top right

44. At what point in the swing does the ball on the string have the most energy?

_____

_____

_____

_____

_____

_____

_____

_____

_____

_____

_____

_____

Question 45 refers to the following information.

The ancient Greek philosopher Aristotle thought that some organisms came to life through "spontaneous generation." For example, insects might be formed out of dead animals. Even in the early 1600s, there were scientists who thought that mice came to life from dirty cloth and a bit of grain left alone for three weeks. By the middle of the 1800s, however, scientists had developed the cell theory. It has been a respected scientific theory since that time. According to the cell theory, a living organism must come from a living organism, because a living cell can only come from another living cell.

45. Which of the following best explains what a scientific theory is and sheds light on how the history of science can include both the theory of spontaneous generation and the cell theory?

 A. A scientific theory is a guess at how something will turn out.

 B. An explanation of a set of observations can be replaced when more is known.

 C. Scientific theories are not widely tested or discussed and are often wrong.

 D. Scientists in the 1600s were not educated, and today's scientists ignore them.

Question 46 refers to the passage below.

Earth's orbit path around the sun is almost circular, but its axis (north-to-south pole through Earth's center) is not at a right angle to its orbit. When the north pole is at its greatest tilt away from the sun, the south pole is at its greatest tilt toward the sun. During this time, it is winter in the Northern Hemisphere and summer in the Southern Hemisphere. The opposite happens when Earth is at the other side of its orbit around the sun. During spring and autumn, you can think of the axis as tilted to the right or the left, rather than toward or away from the sun. In addition, Earth in autumn is approaching the position where a pole (the North pole in the Northern Hemisphere) is tilted away from the sun, so days are becoming shorter. In spring, the opposite occurs.

46. What does this passage explain?

    A. why the Earth's axis is not at a right angle to its sun orbit

    B. that seasons are mostly explained by the tilt of Earth's axis

    C. why spring and fall have the same weather in the same hemisphere

    D. that the southern spring occurs when the North Pole tilts away from the sun

Questions 47 and 48 refer to the following graph.

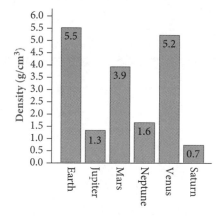

47. The mean density of the sun is about 1.4 g/cm³. In terms of its density, which planet is most similar to the sun?

    A. Earth

    B. Jupiter

    C. Mars

    D. Neptune

48. Three of these planets are solid, and three are made up of mostly gases. Consider their densities, and then name the three solid planets.

_____

_____

_____

49. Within a typical home, heat will move through furniture by _____ and through the air by _____ and _____.

Question 50 refers to the following information.

Ruby-throated hummingbirds and other hummingbird species are often seen at red feeders filled with sugar water. Bird lovers hang these feeders in their yards so they can watch the birds. The idea for these feeders comes from the fact that hummingbirds drink nectar from red flowers. As they do, they pick up pollen on their beaks, and it brushes off onto the flowers they visit after that. In that way, those flowers get pollinated. Bird lovers get an extra treat if their feeders are near spider webs. They can watch the hummingbirds pick insects and spiders out of the webs. Studies have shown that some hummingbirds eat as much in terms of insects and spiders as they do nectar (or sugar water).

50. Which of the following correctly describes the relationship between hummingbirds and the other organisms described?

    A. Spiders are parasitic hosts of hummingbirds.

    B. Hummingbirds are predators of insects and spiders.

    C. Red-flowered plants and hummingbirds have a commensal relationship.

    D. Hummingbirds have a mutualistic relationship with red sugar-water feeders.

51. Which of the following is true about Earth's atmosphere?

    A. The ozone layer is in the atmosphere's lowest layer.

    B. The troposphere contains carbon dioxide and water vapor.

    C. The stratosphere's ozone layer produces the greenhouse effect.

    D. The troposphere's gases protect us from the sun's ultraviolet rays.

Question 52 refers to the following diagram.

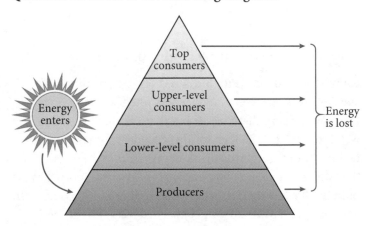

52. Baleen whales eat mostly plankton, of which there are two types: phytoplankton (algae that photosynthesize) and zooplankton (tiny animals). Orcas (killer whales) eat baleen whales. What is the correct order of these species in an energy pyramid, from bottom to top?

    A. phytoplankton, zooplankton, baleen whales, orcas

    B. zooplankton, phytoplankton, orcas, baleen whales

    C. baleen whales, phytoplankton, zooplankton, orcas

    D. orcas, phytoplankton, zooplankton, baleen whales

53. What is the equation that describes the relationship between work and power?

_____

54. Which of the following might cause a person's heart rate to speed up?

    A. the need for more oxygen

    B. gas exchange in the lungs

    C. a buildup of oxygen in the body

    D. the need for more carbon dioxide

55. The downward velocity of a skydiver starts at 0 m/s in the airplane. At 5 seconds after the jump, it is 50 m/s downward. At 10 seconds, it is twice that. This acceleration is caused by the force of gravity. How is this related to the universal gravitation law, $F = G\,(m_1 \times m_2)/r^2$?

_____

_____

_____

_____

_____

_____

_____

_____

_____

_____

_____

Practice Test

Question 56 refers to the following diagram.

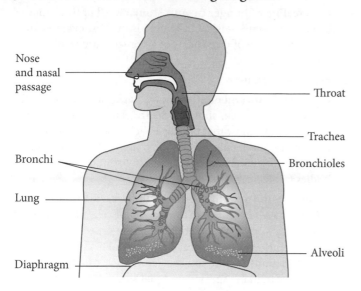

- Nose and nasal passage
- Throat
- Trachea
- Bronchi
- Bronchioles
- Lung
- Diaphragm
- Alveoli

56. Oxygen enters the blood when it moves from

_____ in the respiratory system

into capillaries in the circulatory system.

57. Name two chemicals (not including H_2O) that are found in the ocean as well as on land.

_____

_____

58. Conditions in the womb before birth can affect the phenotype of an organism after it is born. On the other hand, mate selection by the organism's parents will affect its _____.

59. Which of the following is the best explanation of the role of calories in our nutrients?

   A. We should not eat foods that are high in calories.

   B. Calories are calories whether they are in dessert or salad.

   C. A calorie is a measure of the energy that is available from a food.

   D. We should ignore calories and eat food that has important nutrients.

60. The central dogma of molecular biology explains how proteins are made. Why does it therefore explain the mechanism of inheritance?

_____

_____

_____

_____

_____

_____

_____

_____

_____

_____

_____

_____

_____

_____

_____

Answers and Explanations

Unit 1: Life Science Practice, pages 36–40

1. **C. Cell membranes control water flow.** Mitochondria package energy as ATP. Ribosomes make proteins. The nucleus contains DNA. There are no chloroplasts in the human body.

2. **Answer should include 3 or 4 of these factors: size, membrane, DNA, RNA, replication.** Sample answer: The cell theory says there is no living thing smaller than a cell, but the virus is smaller than the smallest cells. This supports the idea that a virus is not a living thing. The virus does not have a cell membrane. This supports the idea that a virus is not a living thing. However, the virus has a lipid membrane similar to a cell membrane. This tends to support the idea that a virus is alive. The virus does not have DNA, and this supports the idea that it is not a living thing. But it does have RNA that contains genes, which tends to support the idea that it is alive. The virus must infect a cell in order to make copies of itself. This supports the idea that a virus is not a living thing. However, the virus can make a copy of itself from inside a cell, which tends to support the idea that it is alive.

3. **chemical reactions**

4. **D. anaerobic respiration** Fermentation, the process used to make yogurt, uses anaerobic respiration by yeasts.

5. **Answers may vary.** Sample answer: A zebra's cells use aerobic respiration most of the time to get energy from sugars to allow it to move around. In a lion attack, a zebra might run long enough to use up the energy provided by aerobic respiration. Its cells could switch to anaerobic respiration to let it run for a while longer.

6. **gametes, 23**

7. **A. parasitism** In parasitism, commensalism, and mutualism—which are types of symbiosis—one organism spends some time in or on another live organism.

8. **D. RNA** When bases pair with the unzipped DNA, RNA is created.

9. **Answers may vary.** Sample answer: Both are needed to make proteins. Both are made up of long twisted chain of bases. But their roles are different—DNA only carries information, while RNA's codons carry information and work to connect amino acids. Also, DNA has a double helix, with two long chains of bases bonded together, while RNA has a single helix.

10. **D. aa, ab, ac, ad** Any genotype that includes a in any way will result in the dominant (a) phenotype.

11. **GG, Gg, or gg** A genotype is the combination of two alleles that an organism can carry for one gene.

12. **0%; 50%** In the first square, 100% of the offspring will have a Gg genotype. The dominant allele will be expressed, and they will all be green. In the second square, 50% (2 of 4) will have the Gg genotype and be green; and 50% (2 of 4) will have the gg genotype and be gray.

13. **A. if a mutation occurs during meiosis** A new allele is made during DNA mutation, which may occur in meiosis before crossover.

14. **small intestine, large intestine**

15. **C. a feeling of hunger in your stomach** All of these may be parts of homeostasis, but hunger is the best example of a receptor—one of three parts of a homeostatic feedback mechanism.

16. **nervous, muscular**

17. **C. Black bears and panthers have backbones, and jellyfish do not.** A cladogram showing the traits that separate these species would show that having a backbone was closer to black bears and leopards than the other traits—color, land vs. water, and hard bodies (which can form fossils) vs. soft bodies (which can't).

18. **Answers will vary but should include at least four of the following:** All organisms are made up of cells; many species have many similar DNA sequences; many species have the same amino-acid sequences; cell components perform the same functions in different species; there are homologous structures in many species; vestigial structures imply connection to common ancestors; the fossil record shows evolution from common ancestors; there is a high correlation between ecological divergence and reproductive isolation.

19. **white oak, bottlebrush, and baobab tree** Pollination is the trait that is between sphagnum moss and white oak. All the species after that (to the right of pollination) share that trait. The others don't.

20. **artificial selection**

21. **D. predation** If predation increases, a population may have to adapt to that pressure. Individuals with traits that help them escape from predators will survive more than others. That is differential survival, sometimes called survival of the fittest. Those individuals will reproduce, and their traits will become more common in the population. That is the process of natural selection.

22. **reproductive isolation**

23. **C. mountain lions, foxes, birds, plants with seeds** This list includes producers (plants), lower-level consumers (birds that eat seeds), upper-level consumers (foxes that eat birds), and top consumers (mountain lions that eat foxes). A. has no producers. B. includes decomposers (fungi). D. has neither upper-level nor top consumers.

24. **A: trees → B: fungi → C: ground squirrels → D: foxes** A food chain should begin with producers and may include decomposers.

25. **C. More matter is stored in wood during chemical reactions.** Less matter is stored in the wood as it is broken down into smaller particles through decomposition.

26. **D. Food-borne bacteria thrive at room temperature.** The preventive measures for all the foods, including non-animal products, include refrigeration, which keeps foods below room temperature. Washing is suggested only for produce.

Answers and Explanations

27. **B. Some populations will change, which will change the populations of others.** Decreased prey populations will affect the carrying capacities of their predators. Competition will increase for some resources, such as drinking water. That will affect animals that swim. Flying birds may escape the storm but will still compete for resources if they return.

28. **Sample answer:** Populations fluctuate—decreasing when members die or move out and increasing when new members move in or are born. When the normal number of offspring isn't born, the population doesn't fluctuate normally and may shrink.

29. **B. Biodiversity will decrease but may recover.** Both the number of species and the number of organisms within species will probably decrease at first but may recover over time. The normal plant species, not alien species, often help to restore balance. Some swimming birds will survive.

30. **Sample answer:** Biodiversity is biological diversity. It is a measure that reflects both the existing number of organisms of a species and the existing number of different species. When a species becomes extinct, the number of existing species shrinks, so biodiversity decreases.

Unit 2 Physical Science Practice, pages 67–72

1. **B. Her forward momentum will decrease.** Her speed will decrease (mass will stay the same), and momentum = mass × speed.

2. **C. speed** Time is the independent variable. Mass is not a variable. Momentum is a product of the two variables.

3. **C. Chemical energy is a type of potential energy.** Chemical energy is energy that is stored in chemical compounds.

4. **A. The lug wrench turns the lug nut clockwise.** The forces are equal, but the total force is not zero because the forces rotate the lug nut in the same direction.

5. **A. change in mass** A push or a pull (force) can change an object's direction, velocity, or momentum (by changing its velocity).

6. **A. The amount of output work a machine performs is always less than the amount of input work.** The more energy lost, the less efficient the machine will be. There will be output only when there is input. The information and diagram do not differentiate between simple and electric machines.

7. **Sample answer:** When energy used over time is not much more than the work done over time, there is not much waste heat, and a machine is highly efficient.

8. **A. which atoms are bonded to each other** Types, number, and ratio are given in all three.

9. **B. Neither is an element.** An element has only one type of atom.

10. **protons, neutrons, electrons** (in any order)

11. **A. The boiling point of water is 100°C.** The statements in B and C are correct, but they are not implied in the information given.

12. **C. whether it is combustible** Unlike physical properties, chemical properties can only be observed during chemical reactions.

13. **B. Some sample was left in some of the beakers during pouring into the weighing pan.** A. could make some density calculations higher than expected, but none are. For C., weighing pans should prevent spilling, and the scale was calibrated each time. D. would not affect the results of the samples that were done.

14. **Sample answer:** Barley weighs the least. Weight decreases as mass decreases, and mass decreases as density decreases if the samples have the same volume. So the sample with the lowest density will weigh the least.

15. **B. $2HgO \rightarrow 2Hg + O_2$** In a decomposition reaction, a complex reactant is broken down into smaller products: $AB \rightarrow A + B$.

16. $2P + 3Cl_2 \rightarrow 2PCl_3$

17. **Sample answer:** No. Although they are all at room temperature and temperature affects solubility, there is another factor. Many substances are more soluble in one solvent than in another.

18. **C. 100**

19. **C. 30** The answer can be extrapolated from the curve.

20. **C. The thermometer was slightly inaccurate.** The three measurements were nearly the same, so they were probably carefully observed and recorded. Escaping heat would not affect the boiling temperature. The accepted boiling point is based on years of experience.

21. **A. energy transferred between objects at different temperatures** Thermal energy is the total kinetic energy (random motion) of the particles of an object, at any temperature.

22. **D. movement of heat from warmer to cooler particles in a liquid or gas** A. is radiation; C. is conduction.

23. **Answers will vary.** Students should recognize that heat can be made to move machine parts, and that movement can be used to move something else (Work = force × distance).

24. **A. energy at W – energy at X** W–Z is the largest energy change; X–Z is net energy change; and Y is not a significant point.

25. **Energy cannot be created or destroyed because of the law of conservation of energy.**

26. **kinetic energy, potential energy, and energy in fields**

27. **Sample answer:** Potential energy in sugar in your body is transformed to kinetic energy in your cranking hand. Kinetic energy in your hand is transformed to electrical energy at the electric coil and magnet (generator). Electrical energy is transformed to electromagnetic field energy when it shines as light from the bulb.

28. **endo**

Answers and Explanations

29. **C. In longitudinal waves, the disturbance is in the direction of the wave energy; in transverse waves, it is not.** In both wave types, particles (if they are present) move (are disturbed), but their net movement is zero, and wave energy travels in one direction.

30. **B. They have different frequencies.** If they had the same wavelength or wave speed, the compression of the top wave would fall directly above the crests of the lower wave. You cannot compare their amplitudes using this diagram.

31. **energy (or electromagnetic energy), space (or a vacuum)**

32. **C. landfill gas** Coal, oil (petroleum), and natural gas contain energy from million-year-old fossil plants and animals. Landfill gas is combustible gas that forms naturally in trash and, especially, plant and animal parts and waste.

33. **Answers may include any three of these: hydropower, wind power, geothermal energy, solar power, biomass, landfill gas, and (theoretically) hydrogen for fuel cells.**

34. **A. coal** Natural gas is a moderate source of air pollution. Solar energy and uranium do not produce air pollution at electric power plants.

Unit 3 Earth and Space Science Practice, pages 91–95

1. **C. Rocky Mountains** Where an oceanic plate slips under a continental plate, mountain building occurs.

2. **A. Tectonic plates met and built mountains to its east and west.** When continental plates push together, mountains are formed. Mountains cause water to run downhill away from them.

3. **Sample answer:** Coral reefs are made of the exoskeletons of coral organisms. These contain large amounts of calcium.

4. **B. precipitation and air pressure data for Alaska over the past 100 years** Temperature, humidity, precipitation, and air pressure data are all helpful, but they should be for the area (Alaska) and not the global atmospheric layer. They should also be for the longest duration possible.

5. **Answer should include:** Two of the following for weather: temperature, humidity, cloud cover, precipitation, air pressure, wind speed, and wind direction PLUS two of the following for climate: latitude, altitude, and distance from large bodies of water. The major difference is that weather occurs in a particular time and location while climate applies over many years.

6. **D. A cold surface current dries the air before it blows over the desert.** Surface currents have a greater effect on local climate than up- or downwelling currents do. As air moves over a cold current, it gets colder and therefore dries out.

7. **B. flooding after a rainstorm** Wind is caused by uneven heating, which leads to differences in air pressure. Wind direction is affected by Earth's rotation.

8. **C. daily samples for a year in many places over land and ocean** Samples taken for just one day may not represent the general conditions, and data from many different places improve the comparison of one type of place (ocean or land) with another.

9. **A. compare CO_2 levels over that area with CO_2 levels over other areas** To see if it's better than average, the area must be compared with different areas.

10. **C. In 5,730 years, half the original amount of carbon-14 in the sample will be gone.** By the end of each half-life, half the C-14 will have changed into another element. The amount keeps being divided in half, so the entire amount is never gone. Only C-14 is affected, not all of the carbon or any other elements in a sample.

11. **Answers will vary, depending especially on which organism is described.** Answers should include some of the following: Plants take in water through their roots and lose it to the air when it evaporates (transpires) from their leaves. Marine animals take in water as they breathe through their gills (as in fish) or as they eat (as in marine mammals). They return water to the ocean during gill breathing and/or when getting rid of wastes as urine or feces. Land animals drink water and lose it to the air (as water vapor) when they breathe out and lose it to the land or water when they urinate.

12. **D.** CO_2 in the atmosphere has increased gradually and fairly steadily, without leveling off, over the past 50 years.

13. **$4,285°C$ ($4,300°C - 15°C = 4,285°C$)**

14. **C. Less than a third of the resources have been renewable.** Biomass is the renewable resource. Less (not more) fossil fuels than biomass have been extracted. Nothing has doubled in this time period, and the graph gives no specific information about gold or silver.

15. **Sample answer:** The extraction of all four types of natural resources—biomass, minerals, metals, and fossil fuels—increased steadily for several decades after 1980. The ratio of biomass to fossil fuel extraction did not change much in that time.

16. **Sample answer:** Both have winds strong enough to break off and displace trees and buildings, and both occur during thunderstorms. Tornadoes are more common, affect smaller areas, and have circling winds that touch the ground. Derechos have straight-line winds.

17. **Sample answer:** Water in the ground (groundwater) may enter a plant and be transpired to the atmosphere. The soil contains carbon from dead plants and animals. It may become part of peat or a fossil fuel and be released to the atmosphere when the fuel is burned. Rock materials at tectonic plates melt and can enter the atmosphere when a volcano erupts.

18. **D. spiral**

19. **D. the one on the bottom left** The sun is located half to two-thirds of the way from the center of the galaxy, on one of its spiral arms.

20. **mantle** The asthenosphere is a thin outer layer of the mantle that is very plastic, so it behaves almost like a fluid.

Answers and Explanations

21. **D. data collected from observing galaxies and clusters of galaxies of different ages** The most helpful data will come from the greater universe beyond our galaxy, so that comparisons can be made with what is happening and has happened already.

22. **weathering**

23. **Sample answer:** Weathering is the breaking down (or dissolving) of Earth materials such as rock. Erosion is the moving of the particles. Weathering and erosion make canyons. Deposition is the depositing of particles in another place. Deposition creates deltas and adds soil to floodplains.

24. **B. Venus, which has a thick atmosphere of mostly carbon dioxide** Mercury and Jupiter have little or no carbon dioxide, which is the main greenhouse gas. Mars has less carbon dioxide than Venus.

25. **A. Most burn out while they are in the mesosphere.** Meteors burn out, not fall apart, because of friction with atmospheric particles. Once in the atmosphere, they don't move away from Earth. A few, but not most, move into the troposphere and may hit Earth's surface.

Practice Test, Pages 96–107

1. **D. Its activation energy is provided by light that starts the reaction.** Whether it is endo- or exothermic depends on the difference in the energy it stores before and after the reaction of energy, not the type it gives off. For C., the heat was a result of the reaction, not the activator.

2. **C. mitosis, which results in daughter cells**

3. **C. There are two copies of each type of chromosome.** Crossing over and two cytokinesis steps happen in meiosis—but the diagram shows mitosis, not meiosis. There are various numbers of cell components, not always two, in mitosis.

4. **A. 0.4 m/s** Speed is distance divided by time.

5. **A. They will both reverse direction at slightly different speeds.** They did have approximately the same momentum ($m \times v$) before the collision ($400 \times 0.5 = 200$ and $450 \times 0.4 = 180$). However, within a system, the total momentum does not change. If the balls stopped, the momentum would be 0. If they both went in the same direction, the momentum would also change, because velocity includes direction.

6. **C. Most of the elk will leave the area, and the population will decline permanently.** Even if elk don't leave the area, there will be less food, so the population will decline permanently. If they move to another area, they will add to the elk population there at first. But it will decrease over time to match the food supply.

7. **Sample answer:** Earth's core is mostly iron, while its surface contains many elements. The core is much thicker and hotter than the surface. Also, the outer core is fluid, while the surface is solid.

8. **C. Plant and animal cells contain many of the same structures.** All types of cells need energy. Living cells come from living cells and cannot be made. Many cells cannot photosynthesize.

9. **Sample answer:** Water was pumped faster than it could seep back. Water is a renewable resource, but it can be used faster than it is renewed.

10. **D. The dry well only reaches below the highest water table level.** The highest water table level occurs only during a period of abundant rainfall. In other times, the well would have been drilled deeper.

11. **B. white foxes** The change in fur color happened in a population over several generations, not in individuals within their lifetimes as it did for deer jumping fences. Swimmers' surviving is an example of differential survival. There is nothing adaptive about breeding two species together.

12. **C. long orange hair and no horns** The combination of 1 3 6 results in long orange hair and no horns. All the possible combinations begin with 1 for long curly hair, so neither A nor B is possible. The combination for D would be 1 4 2 6, which is not given as a possible answer. Therefore, long purple and blue hair and horns is not a possible staagle phenotype.

13. **A.** In B, there are two different genes, not alleles, involved. In C, the righthand horns-horns combinations should be horns-No Horns. In D, long and curly are carried on different genes, not different alleles, so the combinations involve three genes rather than one.

14. **D. 0%** Having horns is recessive, and there will be no homozygous recessive offspring.

15. **aerobic; anaerobic**

16. **C. a positively charged ion** It would then have 10 negative charges and 11 positive charges, so it would have a total positive charge.

17. **energy**

18. **B. It gets quieter and quieter.** Unlike electromagnetic waves, sound waves cannot travel without a medium. As the air is pumped out, there is less matter for the sound waves to travel through.

19. **A. 8 days** In 8 days, only 50% of the sample is radioactive.

20. **D. They have the same elements as the reactants but different properties.** They must have the same elements. The products will weigh the same as the reactants, because mass is conserved.

21. **Answers should include three of the following:** fecal-oral, direct contact with blood, contact with saliva or mucus, airborne transmission

22. **B. taking similar samples in the summer** All the options might improve the results, but samples taken in summer when salting isn't done would give better "controls" for comparison.

23. **B. 2 and 4** Tap water samples would not reflect general environmental levels. The intersection's location on a hill was helpful, since downhill samples were gathered.

24. **C. 2 and 3** The samples that were taken provided enough comparison since they were taken at increasing distances from the salt source.

Answers and Explanations

25. **D. great horned owls** Great horned owls are in more than 12 food chains in this web. Chipmunks are in 9 food chains, mice/voles are in 8, and white spruces are in 5.

26. Answers will vary but should include arrows from left (eaten) to right (eater).
Sample answer: Gray willow → Moose → Wolf

27. **C. when a force moves an object** The formula for work is work = force × distance.

28. **arrow from condensation to precipitation**

29. **Sample answer:** It was likely a tornado. Iowa is not near the coast where hurricanes are likely to do the most damage. Also, Iowa is not very close to any known tectonic boundary, where earthquakes are likely to occur.

30. **Sample answer:** Boil some of the liquid to see whether a solid residue is left behind. Boiling is part of the process of distillation, the typical way to separate a solution.

31. **D. trees to lumber** Sugar in potatoes is stored chemical energy, which is changed to the kinetic energy of body motion. Wind to electric power changes kinetic to field energy. Coal's stored chemical energy is transformed to heat.

32. **C. six or fewer legs; fur or hair; high intelligence**

33. **B. Information carried by DNA is transcribed to make a muscle protein.** There is only one way that protein can be made: Information in DNA is transcribed to RNA, and then the information is translated into protein.

34. **D. when no more solute will dissolve**

35. **B. In conduction, the particles stay in one place.** Heat rises in air during convection when particles move around and touch each other. Radiation happens in air or space but not in liquids.

36. **C. its original mass** Very massive stars become neutron stars or black holes, while stars of average mass become white dwarfs.

37. **B. ecological divergence.** Variation of genetic traits allows ecological divergence, which includes reproductive isolation. Selective breeding is artificial selection.

38. **Sample answer:** Radiometric dating with isotopes can be used to find the ages of fossils. When fossils are found in rock formations, their known age can tell scientists how old those rocks are. Scientists have also used isotopes to find the ages of space rocks.

39. **Sample answer:** A moon orbits a planet, but most asteroids are between two planets. Asteroids are much smaller than moons. Most asteroids are not spherical like moons. Both moons and asteroids orbit the sun.

40. **C. 3** The bowerbird's behavior maintains its territory but not its biological state.

41. **A. mass** You want a small but heavy amount of material, so you need it to be dense. You can't measure density directly, but you can calculate it by measuring mass and dividing by volume. You don't need to measure volume, because you made all the samples the same volume—1 cm^3.

42. **D. 4.2** $(1.7 + 2.3 + 2.7 + 1.5 + 9.0 + 7.8) / 6 = 4.2$

43. **A. at the bottom** Velocity is highest where kinetic energy is highest, which is at the bottom.

44. **Answers may vary.** Students should recognize that the ball has the same amount of energy at all points, but the amounts of potential and kinetic energy change. That is, potential energy decreases as kinetic energy increases.

45. **B. An explanation of a set of observations can be replaced when more is known.** Scientific theories are not guesses. Scientific theories may be proved wrong, but that is after they are widely tested and discussed.

46. **B. that seasons are mostly explained by the tilt of Earth's axis**

47. **B. Jupiter** Neptune's density is close at 1.6, but Jupiter's is closer to 1.4.

48. **Earth, Mars, Venus** Solids are more dense than gases.

49. **conduction; convection; radiation** (the 2nd and 3rd can be interchanged) In solids like furniture, heat moves by conduction; in gases like air, it moves by convection and radiation.

50. **B. Hummingbirds are predators of insects and spiders.** Spiders are prey. The plants and birds have a mutualistic relationship. The birds and feeders can't have a mutualistic relationship because the feeders aren't organisms.

51. **B. The troposphere contains carbon dioxide and water vapor.** The troposphere is the layer closest to Earth's surface and also contains the oxygen that we need to breathe and nitrogen. The ozone layer is in the stratosphere.

52. **A. phytoplankton, zooplankton, baleen whales, orcas** Producers contain the most energy, and it decreases going toward the top of the pyramid.

53. *power = work / time*

54. **A. the need for more oxygen** An increased heart rate will pump oxygenated blood out to the body faster.

55. **Answers may vary.** Answers should show an understanding that as the distance between the skydiver and Earth decreases, the force increases. That is why the skydiver accelerates.

56. **alveoli**

57. **Answers will vary.** Common possibilities include sodium chloride (table salt) and calcium, as well as potassium, magnesium, bromine, and sulfur.

58. **genotype** Genotype is due to a combination of alleles from the two parents.

59. **C. A calorie is a measure of the energy that is available from a food.** High-calorie foods don't always have to be avoided, especially if they are full of other nutrients. But we shouldn't ignore how many we take in.

60. **Answers will vary.** Students should show an understanding that when an egg and sperm combine to make a new organism, that organism contains DNA from both parents. The new organism's proteins are made from that combined inherited information.